C000170785

INSIDE SELLAFIELD

Taking the Lid off the World's Nuclear Dustbin

INSIDE SELLAFIELD

Harold Bolter

Quartet Books

First published by Quartet Books Ltd in 1996
A member of the Namara Group
27 Goodge Street
London W1P 2LD

Copyright © by Harold Bolter 1996

All rights reserved. No part of this book may be reproduced in any form or by any means without the prior written permission of the publisher.

A catalogue record for this book is available from the British Library

ISBN 0 7043 8017 X

Printed and bound in the UK by BPC Paperbacks Limited

Contents

Prologue

Sellafield, previously known as Windscale, is Britain's most controversial industrial site. This is a description its owner, British Nuclear Fuels (BNFL), dislikes intensely, but it is none the less fair. The myriad moral, political, social, health, safety, environmental and economic issues raised by Sellafield have been the subject of increasingly heated debate since the site was opened up for the production of weapons-grade plutonium more than forty years ago. Now that Sellafield is set to become not only the country's biggest plutonium production and storage site but also the burial ground for nuclear waste which will be dangerously radioactive for hundreds of thousands of years, they are certain to be argued over by future generations. It is these bitterly contested areas of public policy which I intend to discuss in this book.

I approach the task from a privileged position. When I left BNFL in 1994, in circumstances which I describe in the Epilogue, I was the company's longest-serving director, responsible for its extensive public information programme, political liaison, community relations, personnel, the legal directorate, security and safeguards. The safeguards branch is responsible for ensuring that weapons materials and sensitive information are kept out of the hands of terrorists and proscribed governments. Every one of these functions was dominated by the activities of Sellafield.

For nearly twenty years I led the team with arguably the toughest public relations task in British industry, that of defending such deeply unpopular causes as the production of materials for the nuclear weapons programme, the discharge of radioactive materials into the Irish Sea and the use of the courts to fight compensation claims brought against BNFL by families convinced that their children had died from leukaemia and other cancers caused by radiation from Sellafield.

More positively, I forced through an increasingly open and honest approach towards public information within BNFL, in the face of opposition from Government ministers, some of my board colleagues and the management and trade unions at Sellafield. It is that policy which led to the development of the Sellafield Visitors' Centre, the UK's most unlikely tourist attraction, and its associated television advertising campaign.

Although once its sole reason for existing, the production of weapons-grade plutonium now accounts for less than 10 per cent of Sellafield's total activity. The site could survive without any business from the Ministry of Defence. But in an uncertain world it will continue to have at least a reserve role as a producer of materials for nuclear weapons, influencing decisions about the place it should have in the imminent reorganization of the nuclear power industry.

Far more important to Sellafield's future, however – and to all our futures – is its position at the centre of Britain's civil nuclear power industry, which provides 30 per cent of the country's electricity. Sellafield is both the technological keystone of that industry and its Achilles' heel. Nearly all of the spent fuel discharged from the country's nuclear power stations is sent there for reprocessing, during which plutonium and unused uranium are separated out for further use and radioactive waste is isolated for storage and disposal.

Shut down Sellafield and the nuclear industry would quickly grind to a halt. This explains why the site has been a constant target of anti-nuclear activists over the years. It was my responsibility to defend Sellafield against these attacks – in the security sense as well as in the arena of public debate.

Largely because of environmental pressure, but also because of management mistakes – and political over-reaction to those mistakes – reprocessing has become a hugely expensive operation. Those wishing to see Sellafield shut down argue that reprocessing is also unnecessary, except perhaps for the spent fuel discharged from Britain's first-generation nuclear reactors. They claim that the economics of nuclear power are such that there is no need to recycle plutonium and uranium, that plutonium is not needed for electricity generation and that there are more than ample supplies of freshly mined uranium ore available. It is a view which has gained strength within the Government, particularly in recent years as market forces have been let loose on the energy supply industries.

Dwindling political support was apparent when the Government hesitated for over a year before it allowed the £2,850 million thermal oxide reprocessing plant (THORP) to come into operation at Sellafield in 1994. This threatened to turn BNFL's flagship project – which has come to stand as a symbol of reprocessing – into the world's biggest industrial white elephant. That could still happen. If THORP's commercial base is as fragile as some believe, or if the highly complex plant fails to operate to its projected standard, it will become a huge financial drain on the nation.

To understand Sellafield it is necessary to see it in its context, as part of a company operating within the public sector. With the planned privatization of Nuclear Electric (NE), Scottish Nuclear (SN) and most of what is left of the UK Atomic Energy Authority (UKAEA) before the next general election,

BNFL will almost certainly be the only sizeable nuclear power company remaining in state ownership by the end of 1996. But because of the additional responsibility it is to be given for the difficult and massively expensive tasks of decommissioning and waste management, BNFL's performance will in large part determine whether the privatization of the rest of the industry is successful.

By exploring what has happened at one major industrial site owned by the Government, Sellafield, and the company which runs it, I hope I can capture some of the sense of unreality which the directors of all state-owned industries must feel. Those fortunate enough to have taken their companies into private ownership have invariably done so with a sense of relief – and not just because they have come out of the privatization exercise as very rich men. There are some salutary lessons here for anyone in the Labour Party with a lingering affection for Clause Four.

Too often the people appointed to run our public sector industries have to cope with political and bureaucratic decisions which fly in the face of sound business practice, creating pay, pricing and contractual distortions which take decades to work out of the system. With a monopoly shareholder, the state, controlling a monopoly supplier, BNFL, as well as its monopoly customers, the nuclear electricity generators and before them the UK generating boards, it is small wonder that capital has often been treated as though it is Monopoly money.

Government control has always caused debilitating uncertainty in the nuclear power industry – and not least during the first half of the 1990s, when a four-year moratorium was placed on the ordering of nuclear power stations by the Government in the wake of the electricity supply industry's privatization, which took place in 1990. That left the country's nuclear power stations behind in the public sector, detached from the rest of the electricity generating industry, wrongly in my view.

But it did have one positive effect, concentrating the minds of those given the task of running the stations. Their performance has been improved considerably during the recent hiatus, turning Nuclear Electric and Scottish Nuclear into more credible candidates for privatization than once seemed possible. They have slashed manpower and halved the operating costs of nuclear plants which had become a laughing stock. They have changed their financial discounting procedures to reduce the immediate costs of waste management and decommissioning. And they have challenged existing contracts for BNFL's fuel supply services, particularly reprocessing at Sellafield, and obtained substantial reductions. This has inevitably led to friction between BNFL and its customers – and to personal animosity among the leaders of the industry – but it has also led to a leaner, more efficient nuclear generating industry.

There is a keen awareness among all the industry's leaders that the run-up to the privatization of nuclear power will be a crucial time for the nuclear industry. Although the main shape of the reorganization was settled in the White Paper which followed the Government's twelve-month review of nuclear energy, there are still questions to be answered. There is also a recognition that this will be the last chance for nuclear power. The next few years will determine whether a form of energy which promised so much has any future or whether the bold attempt to harness the terrifying forces of the atomic bomb has failed.

In my view Sellafield holds the key to settling that issue once and for all. It is in the areas of decommissioning and radioactive waste management and disposal, now effectively concentrated at Sellafield, rather than in the generation of electricity by nuclear energy, that most of the unresolved technical, financial and social problems of the nuclear industry remain. One thing is certain: the days when successive governments were prepared to give the nuclear power industry special treatment because of its perceived long-term strategic importance are over. The industry is, after all, forty years old. It has had long enough to learn how to stand on its own feet.

That is not widely recognized, however. During the recent nuclear review the industry was still busy special pleading, begging the Government to place some weight on such strategic factors as the possible energy needs of future generations, the security of supply provided by a mixed-fuel energy policy and the environmental advantages of nuclear power over the fossil-fuel-burning stations with respect to global warming. This time its pleas fell on deaf ears and as a result the industry is in for a tough time in the short to medium term.

The use of gas to generate electricity, regarded until relatively recently as a profligate use of a premium fuel needed as chemical feedstock, has all the short-term price advantages. To rub home that message BNFL itself has built a gas-fired electricity power station to provide steam and heat for Sellafield when the ageing Calder Hall nuclear station on the site is shut down, and the nuclear generating companies have also said that they want to get into gas-fired electricity generation when they are privatized.

Shortly before I left BNFL I was asked to become Director-General of the British Nuclear Industry Forum, the industry's trade association, and to lead the campaign to obtain the best possible result from the Government's nuclear review. That was not to be. But I believe that it is possible to stimulate debate on important nuclear industry issues from the outside, and that is at the heart of my decision to write this book, together with my long-standing conviction that nuclear power has a future only if it is better understood. Nowhere is that more true than at Sellafield.

There is no doubt that I have lost some of my early enthusiasm for nuclear power. So many mistakes have been made, so many promises broken. But I still have a fundamental belief in the need for nuclear power and a conviction that more of it may be needed in the medium term, as part of a balanced energy policy which pays regard to something more than market forces. I would have thought that history has demonstrated conclusively that over-dependence on any one energy industry is politically and economically dangerous.

I hope it will be seen that although I am deeply critical of some of the decisions which have been taken by politicians, civil servants and the leaders of the nuclear power industry over the years, I readily acknowledge that they were often forced through in the hot-house atmosphere created by extreme political and social pressures. I have described events as accurately and fairly as I can, recognizing the nuclear power industry's many achievements. I have given credit where I believe it is due. I have attempted to analyse my own performance and contribution to the nuclear industry as objectively as I have those of others, admitting the mistakes which I have made.

I am grateful for the help I have received from BNFL, United Kingdom Nirex Limited (Nirex) and other organizations and individuals in the nuclear power industry who provided me with a wealth of information. For the historical background to the early days of nuclear power, I am indebted to Margaret Gowing's *Independence and Deterrence: Britain and Atomic Energy 1945–52* and to Lorna Arnold's *Windscale 1957: Anatomy of a Nuclear Accident*.

What I have made of the information provided to me is entirely my responsibility. For the most part I was encouraged by the extent of the cooperation I received from the nuclear power industry, although BNFL was distinctly wary about the questions I asked about the circumstances surrounding my resignation, which I can understand, and about how robust THORP's financial position is, which I cannot.

I am grateful to Ian Breach for his early confidence that I had this book in me and to Piers Blofeld, of Quartet, and Christopher Little, my Literary Agent, for improving the book which eventually emerged.

Finally, my experience at the end of my career provided me with the rare opportunity of discovering who my true friends were. They were many, but to mention just a few from the more public side of my life, I am particularly grateful for the concern and support which was shown to me and my family from within the nuclear industry by John Hayles, Gordon Williams, Joan Byrne, Dorothy Ashurst, Tony Mills, Peter Green, Arthur Denny and Jimmy Johnston and from outside it by Jean Caines, Neville Gaffin, Geoffrey Tucker, John Banks, Jack Cunningham, MP, and Sir Christopher Harding. My gratitude for the practical and emotional support provided by our long-standing personal friends, too numerous to mention, goes without saying.

Above all, I thank my immediate family – my wife, Sheila, our children, Helen, Matthew and Sarah, and son-in-law, Philip – for their love and belief in me. Without it, and without the delightful distraction provided by my grandchildren, James and Laura, I would not have been around to write this book.

Introduction

Life Outside Sellafield

My route to Sellafield and the boardroom of BNFL was an unusual one. I made my way there by way of a career in journalism, during which I became Industrial Editor of the *Birmingham Post* and later of the *Financial Times*, where I spent eight thoroughly enjoyable years. Other journalists have made it to the top of British industry, but I am not aware of any fortunate enough to reach a position comparable to mine, one of half a dozen executive directors running a state-owned company with a turnover of over £1,000 million a year. It is an achievement of which I am proud. There was very little in my early life to prepare me for what was to come.

I was born at West Bromwich on 16 August 1937 – or possibly on 18 August of that year. According to my mother, a mistake was made on my birth certificate, and as I was the last of ten children it must have been easy for my parents or the registrar to get the details of my birth wrong. I grew up in a working-class environment among people who worked in factories, went into the police force or drove lorries and buses.

I was as naturally aware of the importance of energy and its uses as a country-born child must be of the benefits of the land. I learned in an instinctive way that energy can sustain life or take it, through associations which still linger in the memory.

One of my earliest childhood memories is of standing by my father's side, bleary-eyed from being plucked out of bed, waiting to be taken to the air-raid shelter at the end of Beeches Road, where we lived. He was talking to my mother and we could see a red glow in the distant evening sky. My father, too old for war service, speculated that Birmingham, five miles away as an aircraft flies, was being bombed. He told me later that what we had actually witnessed that night in November 1940 was the destruction of Coventry, twenty miles away – a city virtually wiped out by the energy released by conventional explosives. I was just over three years old.

Five years further on and I recall the rejoicing when we heard that something called an atomic bomb had been dropped on two Japanese cities with strange-sounding names, Hiroshima and Nagasaki, and that the war was finally over. Nuclear energy was launched in the most horrific way imaginable and we all cheered and gloried in the discovery of this new form of explosive energy. It was around the time of my eighth birthday and my two brothers came home shortly afterwards – Bill from the Navy and Tom from the Army, strangers bearing gifts of sweets and exotic fruits.

The peace was no less illuminating than the war in its demonstration of what energy could do to mankind as well as for it. The lights went on in Birmingham again and I was taken to see them by one of my sisters, Eva. We were accompanied by her skeletal fiancé, who had just been released after four years in a German prisoner of war camp. Nobody seemed to care very much about the environment or the health effects of energy production and heavy industry. The boys were back at work, that was the important thing. The Black Country deserved its name. Industrial pollution hung heavy in the air as my friends and I stumbled our way through the smog to the junior school at the end of the road. The air we breathed was something which we could taste, chew and spit out, contaminated by smoke and fumes which came from the energy production which was going to restore Britain's former glory and prosperity.

But the energy which came from solid fuel had to be transported and that was far from easy. During the bitterly cold winter of 1946, the railway tracks and points were frozen solid and little coal or oil could be moved around the country. Most of what there was had to be used to keep the electricity power stations going to supply the needs of manufacturing industry. My parents rented a draughty mid-terrace house from a landlord who was seemingly prepared to see it collapse rather than pay for essential repairs. The house was warmed by a single coal or coke fire – when we could get the fuel. Central heating was something for the future.

On a succession of Saturday mornings during that winter I was woken up in the early hours and taken off by one or more of my sisters to queue for coke at Swan Village gas-works, two miles or so away. The older members of the family were out at work, several of them already married. Swan Village was a place of acrid smells and dark grey dust, named by someone with a wry sense of humour. I was ten years old and had to heave a heavy sack of coke on to a trolley made from a set of old pram wheels and bits of wood and drag the precious load home through slush and ice.

I almost cried with the cold on those mornings, but I knew with absolute certainty that without that fuel we were all going to freeze to death. Thousands did die of hypothermia during that terrible winter. It was a hard way to learn the lesson that without an efficient and economic energy supply system people really do freeze in the dark, a lesson some environmentalists and politicians seem never to have learned.

Later on in life I tried to describe living conditions at that time to my own children – the unheated bedrooms, the leaking roof through which it was possible to see the sky, outside toilets, queuing to get on to freezing-cold buses and wearing old socks on my hands to try to keep warm. They found it impossible to appreciate what it was like. With just a hint of embarrassment, they still refer to it as the time when Dad lived in a cardboard box in the middle of the road – and quickly change the subject. It was a formative period for me, nevertheless, and one which shaped many of my later attitudes towards politics and the energy industries. In particular, I developed a concern for the impact of energy costs on the unemployed, pensioners and the poor, not least the second- and third-generation immigrant families who now live in Beeches Road, West Bromwich, the place where I was born and lived until my early teens.

My own childhood in that road was happy enough, although I was aware that the people living in the houses on the opposite side of the road, the detached houses which backed on to Dartmouth Park, were different. They were clearly much better off than those of us who lived on top of each other along the terrace or in the back-to-back houses of Legge Street, Thynne Street and the other grandly named side-streets which ran off down towards the town centre.

We knew our place in those days and rarely walked or kicked a tennis ball along the pavement on their side of the road and they put Conservative posters in their windows at general election times. My father gained a great deal of pleasure out of turning our front room into a committee room for the Labour Party candidates, Patrick Gordon Walker and John Dugdale. He festooned the windows at the front of the house with Labour Party posters as a defiant statement of the family's allegiance – and had the satisfaction of always seeing Labour win.

The Eleven-plus had just been introduced, although wealthier people could still get their children into the grammar schools by paying their fees. I took the entrance examinations for two schools – West Bromwich Grammar School, within easy walking distance of where we lived, and Holly Lodge County Grammar School, Smethwick, a bus ride away.

I passed both and became the first and only member of my family to go to grammar school, although several of my siblings claimed that they could have done so given the chance, and I believe them. For reasons best known to himself, my father sent me off to Holly Lodge. He may have been impressed by the County in the school's title, by something he had heard about it, or by the fact that the boys' and girls' schools were separate, whereas West Bromwich Grammar School was coeducational. The latter reason swayed him, I suspect. There was to be no female distraction for the child Harold.

Holly Lodge was a much newer grammar school than the more obvious choice at West Bromwich, which several of my friends attended. My memories of Holly Lodge are more of the sporting opportunities which it provided than of any academic challenges, with one exception. I was fortunate enough to be taught by a truly inspiring English teacher, 'Sniffer' Jones, so called because of his persistent sinus problems. I never knew Sniffer's Christian name, but I do know that I owe much of my later success to his encouragement.

I was taught little science at Holly Lodge. This was because of the strange system which the school adopted for streaming its pupils one year after entry. We sat an examination and were divided into three groups on the basis of the result. Those filling the top group became arts students and were taught Latin as well as French and a selection of arts subjects. The middle group learned German and French and concentrated more on the sciences. The remainder, clearly identified as duffers, did French only, with occupational subjects such as woodwork and mechanical drawing thrown in for good measure.

Fortunately, I enjoyed the arts subjects, particularly English and History, which Sniffer also taught, but I do sometimes wonder whether I might have had a different career in nuclear power had I not been placed in the arts stream at Holly Lodge when I was barely twelve years old.

It was Sniffer Jones who found me my first job, after I had finished a mixed bag of O- and A-levels when I was not quite seventeen, a year earlier than normal. In order to go into the sixth form, I had to compress two years' work into one and take examinations in the two levels at the same time. It was an experiment designed to help boys from less well-off families get at least half a sixth-form education.

By then my father had become too ill to work and nearly all of the older members of the family had married and left home. My mother pressed my father to take me away from school as soon as possible so that I could start earning – I overheard their conversation and volunteered to leave – but he resisted her and I had that important extra year at school. Taking O- and A-level exams in the same year was hard-going, however, particularly as I never allowed study to interfere with my love of sport. The experiment was quickly dropped by the school and my indifferent results probably helped the decision along.

But I did do well in English and reasonably well in History, Sniffer's subjects, and this proved to be my salvation. I had confided to Mr Jones that I wanted to be a journalist or a lawyer when I left school, ambitions which seemed way out of reach of someone from my background. Most of my contemporaries considered themselves lucky if they became apprentices at one of the local engineering factories and I was asked by the teacher acting as careers master if I would like to train as a draughtsman at Cadbury's, an awful prospect. The possibility of going to university never entered my thoughts. None of the people I knew or mixed with went there. It was something the children living on the other side of Beeches Road might aspire to, but not us. Sniffer came to the rescue.

I did not know it at the time but he was a friend of W. Vaughan Reynolds, who was then the Editor of the *Birmingham Post*, and persuaded him to take me on as a copy boy, with a view to my becoming an apprentice journalist later if I behaved myself. At my interview Vaughan Reynolds was intrigued by the unusual spelling of my surname – the non-U Bolter. He asked if I was related to William Bolter, whom he knew as a successful contributor to a competition called 'Bullets', which ran in a magazine called *John Bull*. The competition involved the competitor adding three or four words to the three or four words set out in the competition entry form in order to make a witty or amusing statement. I confessed that William Bolter was my father and Vaughan Reynolds seemed much impressed. It turned out that he was a less successful 'Bullets' competitor himself.

I became a copy boy with the *Post* on the following Monday, making tea, running errands, filing newspapers, rewriting the occasional publicity hand-out and learning all I could from the senior reporters and sub-editors, and from Leslie Duckworth, the News Editor, who hid a soft heart behind a tough-guy Yorkshire exterior. I was as pleased as punch, but then the bottom dropped out of my world. My father, barely sixty-three years old, died from peritonitis, brought on by a burst ulcer which had never been diagnosed and so never treated.

His last few years had been miserable ones. Once a vigorous, impressive man, he had been reduced to a wheezing, coughing wreck by bronchitis, probably brought on or made worse by a combination of working among paper dust at the local printing works, where he was employed as a warehouseman – no free grammar schools for his generation – the excessive cigarette-smoking which racked his thin frame towards the end of his life and the general air pollution to which we were all subjected as a result of the burning of fossil fuels.

My father never earned much more than a subsistence wage, augmented from time to time by his wins in the 'Bullets' competition, but he was a remarkably fulfilled man for all that. He delighted in self-education, not with a view to improving his financial circumstances but for the sheer joy to be gained from the acquisition of knowledge. He transmitted that fascination with the world around him to the young son who shared his declining years. It was my father who first exposed me to the wonders of Shakespeare, not Holly Lodge and not even Sniffer Jones; he would declaim Hamlet's soliloquy or some other favourite piece from memory – and do so on the slightest pretext. We would debate current affairs, religion and politics, anything which came to his mind or mine, late into the evening and sometimes into the early hours of the morning.

My father also sparked off my lifelong love of music, practically all music, through his own fairly catholic tastes, although he could never come to terms with pop music or jazz. As a young child, when he was still in good health, I went to watch him conducting brass bands and male voice choirs, which he did with tremendous panache and sensitivity. I listened to opera and classical music programmes with him on the radio, although I found some of it way beyond me. Impoverished as we were at times, we had a piano, a violin, a trombone and a euphonium around the house and were given every encouragement to get on and learn to play them. When I showed an interest in one of the instruments we did not have, the trumpet, my father sent me off to be taught how to play it to the Salvation Army, where he had learned his own music. They fixed me up with a B-flat cornet and for several years I received free tuition from them before I got bored and went off to pursue some other interest, probably the girls at the local Methodist church, which is where I met my wife.

I was eighteen when my father died. Forty years on I still regret that I did not have time to get to know him better. I hope my own children remember me with as much affection as I remember him, but as a workaholic who failed to spare them the time my father gave me when I was growing up, I somehow doubt it.

My father's death came as a dreadful shock, not least because

I felt guilty about the way I had spoken to him towards the end of his life. I had tried to jolly him out of his depression, his conviction that he was dying, reminding him that the doctor had said that there was nothing wrong with him apart from his bronchitis. I tried to talk him back on to his feet, treating him like a hypochondriac, and all the time he was dying. He must have found me totally insensitive and unfeeling.

By then my mother, father and I were living with my sister Eva and her husband, Bob Vince, in their council house home in Heronville Road, Black Lake, ten minutes' walk from the gasworks at Swan Village. As I said, West Bromwich has some extraordinary place-names – swans and herons and lakes, and never a decent stretch of water to be seen near any of them. But the house in Heronville Road was a vast improvement on our terraced home in Beeches Road, with its damp rooms and inadequate heating. We had moved in with my sister when my father became virtually bedridden and my mother found it difficult to cope with nursing him. But the house was obviously grossly overcrowded and it seemed to me that my sister, who had four young children herself, had more than enough to do without me lodging with her as well. I decided to go off and do my National Service, even though my employers had offered to put me forward for a deferment. I also wanted to try to erase the memory of my father on his deathbed in Heronville Road.

I went into the Royal Air Force – and quickly regretted not taking that deferment. I rose to the exalted rank of senior aircraftman during my two years in the RAF, after refusing to sign up for a longer period of service on the off chance of gaining a commission. I was not a very good airman, finding it irksome having to salute and take orders from people who did not seem as bright as me and who failed to win my respect.

It was during my National Service that I began to hear about atomic power and about Windscale – later to be renamed Sellafield, the name by which it has always been known locally. Among the lectures on the dangers for careless young men of contracting venereal disease, complete with stomach-turning photographic slides, we had the occasional talk on the capabilities of the atomic bomb and how we should protect ourselves against radiation if one was ever dropped on us.

Not surprisingly, in view of the need to maintain morale, there were no illustrations at these lectures. All they did was convince me that there was no real defence against The Bomb, although I accepted it for its deterrent value. That has remained an unshakeable conviction ever since.

The newspapers of the time also began carrying stories about how this dreadful new science was going to transform our lifestyles and provide us with unheard-of prosperity. It seemed that the swords were to be turned into ploughshares, through a remarkable piece of alchemy which journalists had some difficulty in describing. In October 1956 I had just finished square-bashing at Padgate, in Warrington, when I read that the young Queen Elizabeth II had opened Calder Hall on the Sellafield site – the world's first nuclear power station. I cannot say that the news exactly blew my mind, but I do remember feeling rather proud of what was described as a historic British achievement.

Almost exactly a year later the world's first serious nuclear accident happened at Sellafield. I was twenty years old at the time and read about the accident while I was stationed at Headquarters 22 Group, RAF Buntingsdale Hall, near Market Drayton in Shropshire, the civilized little RAF station where I worked as a clerk/secretary after being taught the shorthand and typing skills which were to serve me well as a journalist later. Some time after the event we were told that there had been a fire in a plutonium production facility, but because of state security we were not told a lot about what had happened, simply reassured that no one would die as a result of it – an assessment which was challenged many years later.

On my blessed release from National Service, I returned to the *Birmingham Post* and became an apprentice journalist. Unusually, I trained on the *Post*, a morning daily newspaper. Most of my contemporaries were sent out to one of the Birmingham Post and Mail group's weekly newspapers to train. I stayed in Birmingham, covering everything from city centre murders to the dog shows then held in Bingley Hall, near the Bull Ring, where, following the *Post*'s style, I solemnly reported that the 'best bitch of breed' prize had been won by Mrs Jemima Jones or whoever. I even had a spell as television critic, slamming not only *Crossroads*, which was to run for years, but also a variety of young entertainers, including Tommy Steele and the Beatles.

Perhaps unsurprisingly, my long-term journalistic career was seen as not lying in the direction of the arts, and soon after I completed my apprenticeship I began to find that I was being given most of the industrial news story assignments which the *Post* then covered. I remember a few of them in particular because they helped to mould opinions which I was to take with me into the later stages of my journalistic career and into my second career in nuclear power.

My natural instinct, coming from a working-class background and with a father who spent his working life as a trade unionist and member of the Labour Party, was to believe that the trade unions could do little wrong. But as I pursued my own career, writing about the motor industry, machine tools, coal, electricity and general engineering, I began to see that industrial life was more complicated than that.

I found that the best pay rates were not necessarily received by those who worked hardest – my father's 'fair day's work for a fair day's pay' ethos – but rather by those prepared to wield power in as opportunistic a way as possible. Relatively small groups of people in key positions – the car delivery drivers getting new vehicles away from the production lines at Longbridge and Cowley, the meter readers who formed themselves into a militant unofficial shop stewards' committee in the electricity industry, the print workers in newspapers – could and did hold vast industries to ransom.

Much the same was beginning to happen in the coal industry. Although that was a less important industry in the West Midlands, which then had a remarkably diverse industrial base, there were two incidents in my early journalistic career which affected my view of the coal industry and which I remember in particular.

On one memorable occasion, I was on a cross-Channel ferry with hundreds of miners who were taking part in the annual conference of the National Union of Mineworkers (NUM). They had taken a mid-conference break, a day trip to France, and I spent some time talking to Will Painter, the General Secretary of the NUM, a Communist who very much had his members' interests at heart.

He told me never to forget that mining was a dirty, dangerous, degrading activity which no human being should have to undertake. If there were alternative jobs, he would like to see all the pits shut down. But as there was no other work in the mining communities – and unlikely to be – he saw it as his duty to get the best possible pay rates for the NUM's members.

I also recall visiting one of the Coal Board's new pits in Nottinghamshire shortly afterwards, to be shown what was then a new technique for cutting coal, retreat mining, and thinking that if that was the best, what must the worst of the pits be like? John Cole, later to become the BBC's Political Editor, was then writing for the *Guardian* and was also on the trip. I remember thinking that working in the nuclear power industry must be preferable to coal mining, and everything I have seen since confirms that view.

Somewhat to my surprise, I found that I enjoyed the challenge of trying to interpret industrial and scientific achievements to the public, in terms which they could understand, free from jargon. On one occasion I was sent off to the Royal Radar Establishment at Malvern, in Worcestershire, which was opening its doors to the press for the first time, and was enthralled by what I saw and what I was told.

I came back from that visit and told David Hopkinson, who had taken over from Vaughan Reynolds as Editor of the *Birmingham Post*, that I thought I could get a series of features out of what I had learned. I must have sounded extremely enthusiastic as I told David how infra-red technology could be used to identify heat sources at night, helping to fight crime, how it could direct weapons on to their targets, how it could show that smoking cigarettes stopped the blood flowing to the ends of people's fingers and how it had a variety of other fascinating applications.

He told me to forget the features and write the subject up as a series of news stories. I did so and David Hopkinson, an excellent editor, devoted most of the front page to what I had written. There were follow-ups in all of the nationals and on radio and television the following day. One of the people working at Malvern at that time, although I did not know it until years later, was Donald Avery, who went on to become Deputy Chief Executive of BNFL.

Because of my new-found interest in science and industry, it was probably inevitable that I should be told by David Hopkinson that my general reporting days were over and I was to specialize and become the *Post*'s full-time Industrial Editor, helping Keith Gascoigne, the paper's newly appointed Business Editor, to establish a regular industrial supplement in the paper. I had mixed feelings about the appointment. Around the same time the News Editor's job became vacant and I rather fancied that, but it went to Martin Hedges, who was undoubtedly better equipped for the post and who has remained a friend over the years.

In addition to Keith Gascoigne, a fine journalist who had rejoined the *Post* after a spell as the Midlands correspondent of what was then still the *Manchester Guardian*, the industrial team brought together at the *Post* in the early 1960s was an extremely talented one. It included Michael Cassell, who went on to become a highly successful member of the editorial staff of the *Financial Times*, Anthony Rowley and Roger Vielvoye, who joined the Industrial desk of *The Times*, Alan Hughes, who wrote about labour relations for the *Daily Telegraph*, and Andrew Goodrick-Clarke, who became the influential City Editor of *The Times*. A later recruit to the *Post*'s industrial team was Jack Hay, the Motoring Correspondent, whose daughter Sally was to marry Richard Burton.

As Industrial Editor of the *Post* I came into contact with some of the biggest users of energy in the West Midlands, which was then the most flourishing industrial area in the country. Would that it was so today. I wrote about the car industry when there were still half a dozen large, independent and British-owned car-manufacturing companies with interests in the region, supported by hundreds of component suppliers, when there was still a fair-sized UK motorcycle industry and when Coventry, rebuilt after the war, housed a score and more powerful machine tool companies with world-wide reputations for excellence.

Steel was still being made from raw materials which were melted and combined in huge blast furnaces and shaped in the heat and clamour of the rolling mills. Before I got my first car, a temperamental 1937 Standard Flying Twelve, I used to stand and watch the hot metal snaking along the troughs as it passed from roller to roller at Johnson's rolling mills in Black Lake, now long since gone the way of much of West Bromwich's industry. The factory was on my route to and from the home of my girlfriend, Sheila Powis, the young office worker who later became my wife. I worked from two p.m. to ten p.m. and Sheila's mother allowed me to call in and see her on my way home if I could make it by ten-thirty, taking two buses to get there from Birmingham. And then I had to walk the couple of miles home past Johnson's. It must have been love.

The energy industries – coal, gas, electricity and the embryo nuclear power industry – were all parts of the commanding heights of the economy and I never questioned that the post-war Labour Government was right to place them in the hands of the state. But writing about those industries, from the Industrial desks of the *Birmingham Post* and of the *Financial Times*, it became increasingly clear to me that some of these industries were being badly managed, often through Government interference or because of a lack of resolve on the part of Government when firmness was needed.

The trade unions had a stranglehold on nearly all of the state-owned industries, not least the coal industry, which dominated the energy scene, still employing something like 500,000 people when I left journalism twenty years ago. Even though this was well down on the peak of 1 million, the British coal industry was still very important, not least in terms of its trade union influence. Now, with only 10,000 employees, working in fewer than twenty pits, the miners and their leaders have no more relevance within the trade union movement than the unions representing the nuclear power workers, who now outnumber them.

The dominance of the coal industry and the willingness of the NUM to threaten to bring down elected governments was one of the reasons why I became convinced that Britain needed a balanced energy policy, with coal, gas, oil, nuclear power and energy conservation having more or less equal importance. I believe that there is still a need for such a policy and if that means some measure of state control or influence, so be it. But because of my experience of working in a state-owned company, I would prefer that all the energy industries were in the private sector, with the public interest safeguarded through the system of regulators now in place, with the important addition that the regulators themselves should be made accountable to Parliament.

Although I enjoyed being a reasonably big fish in a relatively small pool, I realized as I approached my thirtieth birthday that I had to decide whether to stay with the *Birmingham Post* for the rest of my journalistic career or have a shot at Fleet

Street. I made up my mind to leave the provinces while on a trip to Sweden, where I discussed the prospects of finding a job in London with Dennis Topping, who was then with the *Financial Times*. Dennis told me that he was about to leave the *FT* to join *The Times* and that if I applied for a post with the *FT* immediately, I might be lucky. He also offered to put in a good word for me. At that time the *FT* was expanding but losing staff to *The Times*, which had just started up a business section, and I was recruited.

I joined the *Financial Times* in 1967 and became its Industrial Editor two years later, writing mainly about the major state-owned industries, the Confederation of British Industry and the industry-oriented Government departments. It is a period of my life which I still look back on with affection and some pride. The *FT* was a good paper to work on, with plenty of space to fill and a tradition of giving young men their heads. While I was there I became increasingly fascinated by the relationship between politics and industry and it was not long before I began to attract job offers from some of the industry chairmen I interviewed.

In 1975, after eight years on the *Financial Times*, I became restless and began to look for a new challenge. I was approached to join BNFL as Director of Information. Strangely enough, I had rarely written about the nuclear power industry for the *FT*. Nuclear power was regarded by the *FT* more as a science than a business and David Fishlock, the Science Editor, usually wrote about it. I had misgivings about making the move from journalism to public relations, which I regarded as an inferior occupation. I had carved out a reasonably successful career in newspapers and saw myself as one of the gamekeepers of society, keeping a watchful eye on the major industries on behalf of the public, and I was wary of the poachers in public relations, who seemed often to do little more than try to gain favourable publicity for their clients by plying impressionable journalists with booze and favours.

But at the age of thirty-eight I was beginning to wonder where my career was going. Much as I had enjoyed working for the *Financial Times* and covering the most important industrial stories of the day, I could not see that I could maintain my enthusiasm for writing about industry for the paper until my retirement, which I still expected to be twenty-seven years away. Nor could I see myself gaining further promotion at the *FT* and I was still ambitious. As a non-graduate, I believed that I stood no chance of becoming Editor and to cap it all I fell out with the then News Editor, David Prior-Palmer, a coming man. I came to the conclusion that it was time to move on. BNFL looked a good bet.

Although I wanted to do more than write about it, I was fascinated by state-owned industry and its relations with Government. It was a subject which had filled much of my time as an industrial journalist, both in the provinces and in London. I also regarded nuclear power as the fuel of the future, not least because it was apparently much cleaner than the fossil fuels, the source of much of the pollution which had surrounded me as I grew up.

The Magnox nuclear power stations, developed from the original Calder Hall design, were said to be working well and the advanced gas cooled reactor (AGR) station building programme was barely under way and therefore had not had time to dismay me. And the oil crisis of 1973, when the Organization of Petroleum Exporting Countries (OPEC) quadrupled oil prices, was still fresh in the memory. Nuclear power was new and needed.

At a particularly bad moment in my relationship with Mr Prior-Palmer, who appeared to want to take over my responsibilities for coordinating industrial coverage on the *Financial Times*, I received an approach through John Dunkley, the first-class Chief Press Officer of British Steel, to see if I would be interested in joining BNFL. John had been approached first and had turned the job down. I decided that I had nothing to lose by listening to what the fledgeling company had to offer.

From my first meeting with Coningsby Allday, BNFL's inspirational Chief Executive, who had been in office only a few months, I was convinced that this was a man I could work with. Con, named after the central character in Disraeli's novel *Coningsby*, persuaded me that if I joined BNFL I would be given a more or less free hand to test new theories about communications in a previously secretive industry. Con also promised that if all went well I could expect to enter general management and possibly get on to the board. To clinch the matter, he immediately agreed to pay the salary I asked for, which was 50 per cent more than I was getting at the *Financial Times*. I should have asked for more!

BNFL appeared to me to have tremendous prospects. It was barely two years old, having been formed out of the UKAEA's production group, and the responsible Labour Government minister, Tony Benn, still in his 'white heat of technology' phase, seemed to be very much in favour of atomic energy.

At our early meetings Con explained that my main task would be to defend reprocessing, the recovery of uranium and plutonium from spent nuclear fuel. At that time it did not sound much of a challenge, as hardly anybody seemed to be opposed to this activity, not even Friends of the Earth, which was then the principal environmental organization. But Con Allday and my old friend David Fishlock, who advised me not to join BNFL, had the foresight to see that the massive expansion of reprocessing which was then being planned for Sellafield might lead to trouble.

What was being talked about was a THORP, which would reprocess fuel from the new generation of reactors being built overseas and in the UK. Eventually built at a cost of £1,850 million, or £2,850 million when associated waste treatment plants are taken into account, this was to dominate my working life for the next two decades. It was not commissioned until December 1993, several years late, and right up to the day when the first spent fuel went into it there was considerable doubt as to whether it would operate at all. The plant was still being brought up to speed in 1995 and there are those in the company who wonder if it will ever work as effectively as planned.

I am reasonably optimistic that THORP will perform satisfactorily, but am by no means certain that it will prove to be the financial success which Con Allday and I once anticipated. Too much has changed, too many of the assumptions we all made back in 1975 have proved to be false. If we had known then what we know now, THORP would surely never have been built.

Chapter One

Sellafield's Early Years

Born Out of the Bomb

Sellafield grew out of the need to produce materials for the atomic bomb – and it was only the fourth choice as the site on which Britain's plutonium production factory should be established. From drawing board to separated weapons-grade material took six years – a remarkable achievement by men working at the frontiers of science and technology against time pressures imposed on them by a Government which was convinced that the Russians were preparing to invade. At one level, Britain's race to get to the bomb is an epic story of scientific and technological achievement; at another, the project left behind an industrial, social and moral legacy which we are still having to come to terms with.

Some of the people who built the bomb became my colleagues when I joined the nuclear industry and the last of them retired only a few years ago. To a man they feel that they have been part of something which was vital to the country's continued freedom and security. As a result they are genuinely hurt by the attacks made on them by the peace marchers and parts of the media. Once seen as the nation's saviours, they were to find themselves treated as murderous villains and accused of perpetuating an expensive and dangerous industry. This dramatic deterioration in the public's perception goes a long way towards explaining the secretive, closed attitude which persists among many people in the nuclear industry today. They would love to be loved again.

Sellafield's involvement in the atomic weapons programme had its roots in the decision of a group of refugee nuclear physicists to flee to Britain at the start of the Second World War, where they continued studying the properties of uranium. Uranium, mined in the same way as any other minerals, contains atoms of different types, or isotopes, which are distinguished by different numbers. The ore consists for the most part of uranium 238 (U238) but also contains about 0.7 per cent of uranium 235 (U235). This is the more useful isotope as its atoms are fissile – that is to say, they split or divide to form other lighter atoms when they are irradiated with (or struck by) neutrons. The U235 atoms also discharge spare neutrons, releasing energy.

In the spring of 1940 two of the refugee scientists, Otto Frisch and Rudolf Peierls, working at Birmingham University with British scientists, demonstrated that five kilogrammes of fissile U235 would be enough to produce the super-high-speed nuclear chain reaction needed for an atomic bomb. This was the catalyst for research into ways of separating the U235 out from the U238 in the natural uranium ore, the so-called enrichment process.

In 1941 two French scientists, Hans Von Halban and Lew Kowarski, escaped to England from occupied France, taking with them the world's total known stock of heavy water in twenty-six jerry cans. The two Frenchmen had been members of a scientific team working on slow neutron chain reactions in Paris. The importance of the cans of heavy water smuggled out of France was that heavy water was the most efficient known medium, or moderator, for slowing down neutrons during the atom-splitting process, making the released energy more manageable. While slow chain reactions were useless for the purposes of the bomb, which was the real goal at the time, they did offer the exciting prospect of electricity generation.

Two of Von Halban and Kowarski's colleagues at the Cavendish Laboratory in Cambridge predicted that a system using slow chain reactions in natural uranium would not only release energy in a controllable form which could be used for electricity generation but also create a new fissile element from U238 while doing so. This, they forecast, would behave like U235 and also be a possible new bomb material. This new element was eventually called plutonium. The identification of plutonium led to a further programme of research and to the development of reprocessing, a chemical separation technique which enables plutonium and unused uranium to be recycled and radioactive waste to be isolated from the spent uranium fuel. Reprocessing is what Sellafield is all about.

The early work carried out on nuclear power in Britain was written up in a report by a highly influential scientific committee, codenamed MAUD, in the summer of 1941. The report discussed the possibility of producing atomic bombs using U235 or possibly plutonium and described the plant and processes needed for separating out U235 from uranium ore. It discussed nuclear energy as a source of power, using natural uranium as a fuel and heavy water or graphite as a moderator, and forecast that a 'uranium boiler' should be cheaper than a power plant fuelled by coal or oil.

The MAUD report was taken to the United States, where it galvanized the Americans into action. They began to pour resources into the nuclear project. In late 1941, while the British were still ahead in the research race, the Americans proposed a joint venture towards the development of nuclear power. The British declined, offering information exchanges only. But by mid-1942 the Americans had not only caught up but actually moved ahead in some areas. The British tried to resurrect the idea of a joint approach, but this time the

Americans said no and even the information exchanges were halted. By the end of the war the US had ploughed some $2,000 million into the atomic bomb project and was far and away the leading nuclear nation.

In August 1943 Winston Churchill and Franklin D. Roosevelt signed an agreement promising 'full and effective collaboration' on nuclear power, the so-called Quebec Agreement. As a result of that agreement most of the British scientists went to the US to work on the development of U235 separation or on fast neutrons for bombs at Los Alamos, as part of the Manhattan Project, which led to the bombs dropped on Hiroshima on 6 August 1945 and on Nagasaki three days later. But none of the British scientists was allowed near Hanford, in the state of Washington, where the atomic reactors (or piles) were built to produce military plutonium.

Churchill and Roosevelt extended the Quebec Agreement in September 1944, pledging full Anglo-American atomic cooperation for civil and military purposes after the war. But following Roosevelt's death the agreement was torn up and another collaboration agreement, between Roosevelt's successor, President Harry Truman, and Churchill's successor as Prime Minister, Clement Attlee, turned out to be equally worthless. By then the Americans had decided that only they should have nuclear weapons, which would have made them the sole guardian of the international conscience. But it was not to be. With or without help from the US, the USSR, Britain and France were determined to become nuclear powers.

Clement Attlee was pitched into the strange new scientific world of nuclear power at the deep end when the Labour Party came to power in Britain, only a week before the atomic bombs were dropped on the two Japanese cities and Japan surrendered, ending the Second World War. Only seven ministers in Churchill's wartime coalition Cabinet had been involved in the atomic weapons project – and none of them was a member of the Labour Party. Attlee himself, Churchill's wartime Deputy Prime Minister, was deliberately excluded.

When he became Prime Minister, Attlee behaved just as secretively. Apart from himself, only six other members of his Cabinet knew what was going on – Ernest Bevin (Foreign Minister), Herbert Morrison (Lord President of the Council), Stafford Cripps (President of the Board of Trade), Arthur Greenwood (Lord Privy Seal), Hugh Dalton (Chancellor of the Exchequer) and John Wilmot, who was at the Ministry of Supply, which was given responsibility for the project.

The new Prime Minister's decision to limit ministerial involvement may in part have been because of the suspicions which Attlee and Bevin harboured about the loyalty of some of their left-wing colleagues. In addition, Attlee, an astute politician, recognized the danger of debating the enormous implications of nuclear power in public. He had not had time to master the science of the development any more than his ministers or Civil Service advisers had. The matter was largely left to the few experts who had emerged during the war.

Although Attlee and most British politicians still hoped for a post-war atomic partnership with the US, they also believed that Britain must have a national atomic project. The Americans might not have totally trusted the British, but the feeling was reciprocated. Two months after taking office, Attlee set up a research establishment at Harwell, fifteen miles from Oxford, 'to cover all uses of atomic energy', and pulled John Cockcroft back from Canada where he had been working on the British nuclear weapons programme to be its director. Three months later, in January 1946, the Government announced another establishment, to undertake the production of fissile material 'for whatever purpose it might be required'.

Christopher Hinton, later to become Lord Hinton, was appointed the first Director of this establishment, which was based at an old Royal Ordnance Factory site at Risley, near Warrington, where BNFL still has its headquarters and where I had my office for eighteen years. Hinton, who had worked at ICI before the war and had then been Deputy Director-General of the wartime filling factories, which produced bombs and shells using conventional explosives, was given no written terms of reference but it was made clear to him that his first task was to produce plutonium for bombs. In fact, a formal ministerial decision to make atomic bombs was not taken until a year later, in January 1947, and it was only disclosed to Parliament and announced publicly in May 1948, nearly two and a half years after Christopher Hinton was given his secret brief. There was little more than polite interest.

An enormous amount of secrecy surrounded the post-war atomic bomb project in Britain – at least as far as the public was concerned, if not the spies passing information to the USSR. This secrecy was maintained right through the first decade or more of the civil nuclear power programme, becoming an obsession and explaining why Sellafield has been regarded with deep suspicion for so long. It will take many years of openness and honesty for the site to have any chance of being accepted as part of the normal fabric of British industry, which is BNFL's ambition.

Although the decision had been taken to make atomic bombs, there was still some debate about whether the first one should use highly enriched uranium or plutonium. The Americans had demonstrated that they could make both types of bomb, but Britain could only afford to head off in one research and development direction. Plutonium was eventually chosen and Sellafield was identified as the site where Britain would produce and separate this deadly material, a choice made almost by default. An early plan was to site the nuclear reactor and the reprocessing plant in Canada, where much of Britain's early research work had been carried out. Largely because America was being less than helpful at that time, and the Canadians seemed to be drawing closer to the Americans, that idea was quickly dropped.

Then the advisers suggested a site in North Wales. It did

not take Hinton long to decide that the men of Harlech, the nearest town to the planned development, would not lie there dreaming for very long if the nuclear scientists invaded such an attractive tourist area. A third choice – and the favourite for some time – was a remote spot near Arisaig, in the far north-west of Scotland, less than ten miles south of the Isle of Skye as an unfavourable wind might blow. Unfavourable winds were one of the preoccupations of the early site planners. They knew that if there was an accident, nuclear fall-out could float on the wind and affect local populations. A remote site was therefore regarded as essential. Forty years later Chernobyl was to prove with devastating force that national and international boundaries are no barrier to the insidious, silent threat of radioactive fall-out on the grand scale.

Apart from its remoteness and the fact that it had a good supply of water for cooling purposes, Arisaig was totally unsuitable. It was a greenfield site, with poor communications and ground conditions which were far from ideal for the foundations of heavy buildings. The plutonium production reactors were to be built from thousands of tonnes of graphite, which had replaced heavy water as the favoured nuclear reactor moderator.

Hinton and his team believed an extremely remote site would have to be found because they would need to use water-cooled reactor piles to produce plutonium, as the Americans had done. There was a widely held view even then that in safety terms water-cooled reactors were less forgiving than gas-cooled reactors. This is a view which re-emerged during the public inquiry into the construction of the Sizewell B pressurized water reactor (PWR), commissioned in 1994.

Having chosen a water-cooled reactor system for its Hanford plutonium factory, the Americans had set site selection criteria which could hardly be met anywhere in Britain. They had decided that their plutonium production piles must be built five miles apart and fifty miles from any town with more than 50,000 inhabitants, twenty-five miles from one with a population of 10,000 and five miles from any town with 1,000 people living there. They also stipulated that the site must be linked to a thirty-mile four-lane highway, so that the workforce and local people could be evacuated in a hurry in an emergency.

Because of the problems the Hinton team was having in finding a site which was sufficiently remote, scientists at Harwell had been working feverishly on the design of two systems which might make it possible to construct the plutonium piles closer to centres of population, a pressurized gas-cooled pile and a pile to be cooled by air blown straight through the reactor core at atmospheric pressure.

At the eleventh hour there was a breakthrough at Harwell and an air-cooled reactor design was offered to Hinton and accepted. It was this design, together with a new design of fuel can, which saved the day and made it possible for Hinton to choose Sellafield as the site for Britain's first and only plutonium production factory. An air-cooled pile was considered to be simpler to design, quicker to build and safer to operate. While it needed a relatively remote site, it did not need an Arisaig.

Sellafield was a former Royal Ordnance Factory site with an existing infrastructure and a small reserve of workers who knew something about working in an industry where secrecy was important. There were also signs that the coal and anhydrite mines in west Cumbria were becoming worked out and that iron and steel production had a limited future, so there was a much bigger potential labour force available. In all, Sellafield was one of the few areas of the country which would welcome the new industry. This is not to say that local people understood what they were taking into their midst. The most they knew was that it had something to do with the atomic bombs dropped with such horrific effect on Hiroshima and Nagasaki a couple of years earlier.

Sellafield's main disadvantage was that a building workforce of nearly 5,000 would be needed at the peak of the piles construction programme. Most of these workers had to be attracted into the area from the cities and towns of the industrial North-West and North-East and assimilated into a rural environment. There was less commuting by itinerant construction workers then. The difficulty was resolved in the usual way – much as BNFL attracted a skilled construction industry labour force into the area to build THORP at Sellafield in the 1970s and 1980s. Money was thrown at the problem. The site became known as the gold coast. Sellafield still has a reputation for paying the highest wages in the area.

The Sellafield plants were designed at Risley, where Christopher Hinton had set up his headquarters in February 1946 with five engineers who had worked with him in the wartime filling factories. None of them knew anything about atomic energy. From this small beginning, Hinton built up a production division with 480 scientists and engineers. Under his inspired leadership men were trained in a new science, production sites were found and factories designed, built and put into operation. These people, learning as they went along, not only designed the two plutonium production piles and their associated reprocessing plant at Sellafield but also developed plants to treat uranium ores, to produce uranium metal and to fabricate nuclear fuel elements from this metal as well.

On-site work on the plutonium production piles began at Sellafield in September 1947. By then the site had been given a new name. It was called Windscale after the bluff overlooking the River Calder on the seaward side of the site, supposedly because there might be confusion between Sellafield and the uranium fuel production site which had been established at Springfields, near Preston. The risk of confusion did not deter Con Allday from renaming the site Sellafield in 1981 and as that is the name by which it has always been known locally that is what I will call it throughout the book.

Each of the plutonium production piles was built out of

2,000 tonnes of graphite blocks and the core of each reactor was encased in a 'biological shield', a box of reinforced concrete which was seven feet thick and provided protection against the intense radiation within it. Cooling air was forced through the core by eight large blowers and vented into the atmosphere through stacks or chimneys 410 feet high. That is only 100 feet lower than Blackpool Tower. Lord Hinton later called the massive piles 'monuments to our initial ignorance' and there is no doubt that the scientists and engineers who built the Windscale piles, men with no previous nuclear experience, were still learning as they worked on the project.

Sitting on top of the piles were filter galleries which were installed on the instruction of Sir John Cockcroft. They were put on at the last minute after Cockcroft had visited the US in 1948 and learned that the atomic site there at Oak Ridge was having trouble with particle emissions. Uranium oxide particles were falling to the ground within the site boundaries and Cockcroft thought there was a danger of something similar happening at Sellafield. The galleries on top of Hinton's monuments were promptly called 'Cockcroft's follies'.

Despite the 'initial ignorance' of those involved in the project, the first of the two production piles built at Sellafield began to operate in October 1950, within ten days of its target date and only three years and one month after the first sod had been cut on site. Pile No. 2 started up eight months after that, in June 1951. In January 1952, little more than six years after Hinton's appointment, the first irradiated fuel rods were taken out of the piles and fed into the chemical separation plant, marking the start of reprocessing at Sellafield. On 28 March 1952 Tom Tuohy, the Sellafield site's Deputy General Manager at that time, opened the reaction vessel, and saw and handled the first piece of plutonium made in Britain.

Plutonium for Britain's first atomic test, codenamed Hurricane, was delivered to the weapons division in August 1952 and the finished atomic device, which was not actually a bomb, was flown to Australia for the first test. On 3 October, in a group of uninhabited islands off the north-west coast of Australia, it was detonated in shallow water, with a force equivalent to 20,000 tonnes of TNT. Britain had become a nuclear power, to great sighs of relief and considerable rejoicing. The Russians had exploded an atomic bomb three years earlier and the world was just entering the Cold War. Now Britain had its own nuclear deterrent.

The two piles were not to work for long, however. In October 1957, seven years after it was built, Pile No. 1 caught fire. It is still not known for certain what caused the fire, which raged for nearly two days. It was the first major accident in the history of nuclear power – a first Sellafield could have done without. Volunteers worked heroically to put the fire out, although from conversations I have had with some of those involved, it is obvious that not many of them appreciated the danger they were in.

They pushed thousands of highly radioactive nuclear fuel elements out of the stricken reactor pile, which literally glowed in the dark as they laboured. Every steel rod they could lay their hands on was used for the task, including scaffolding poles dragged across from the construction area on the Sellafield site where Calder Hall, Britain's first nuclear power station, had just been completed. The steel rods came out red hot and dripping with molten metal as the men struggled to push the distorted fuel cartridges to the back of the pile and wrestled burning graphite to safety.

The official version of events is that these volunteers were all fitted out with respirators and protective clothing and equipped with film badges and dosimeters to record the massive amount of radiation which some of them received. In the main that may be the case, but the official version is still disputed by some of those who were there. Arguments about the dose records kept during the fire and about the general standard of radiation dose record-keeping during the early years of the site's operation still crop up in compensation claims. The effects of radiation were certainly not as well understood then as they are now – and even now they are constantly being reassessed, unnerving those who work at Sellafield or who have to defend the standards to which the industry works.

I was given some idea of what it was like to be involved in the pile fire-fighting exercise by my good friend the late Brian Potts, who died a tragic death in a road accident in 1981. I know that Brian insisted on double checking the radiation dose record ascribed to him at the time of the fire and it has been established that no records at all were kept for some of the men who fought the fire.

'It was a matter of all hands to the pump,' Brian told me during one of our several conversations about the incident and what it was like to work in the nuclear industry in its early years. 'There wasn't time to organize things properly. I was called up from the company hostel where I lived, given a pole and told to get on with it. We simply poked the burning fuel elements out of the channels as best we could. It may seem strange, but it all seemed just a bit of excitement. Most of us were young and I can't say that we were particularly frightened, although we knew that it was vital that the fire was put out. If it had spread throughout the reactor core there would have been a hell of a problem, but we were lucky. Remember that many of the men had young families living nearby at Seascale and other local villages.'

Some of the men working at Sellafield at the time still feel it was wrong that their families were not evacuated during the 1957 fire. Local people were not even advised to stay indoors and shut their windows to avoid escaping radioactivity, even though the Sellafield site's managers were not sure how to put the fire out. Women went shopping, pushing young babies in prams and pushchairs, as Pile No. 1 spewed radioactivity into the air. Children played in their gardens in the shadow of the burning plutonium piles.

Local residents were still not given any sort of warning

when the extremely risky decision was taken to pour water on the fire, two days after it had been discovered. There was a real fear even among those who took the decision to pour water on the burning graphite and uranium metal as a last resort that an explosive mixture of carbon monoxide and hydrogen with air might be formed. The risk was taken, with most of the local population oblivious to what was going on and the fire was put out. As Brian Potts said, they were lucky.

When the water hoses were turned on, the Cumbrian police were at last alerted to the possibility of mass evacuation. The fact is that evacuation might have been as dangerous as the fire itself if there had been mass panic. There is still no fast way out of Sellafield, as I know to my cost. A few years ago I sat in my car at the end of a traffic jam several miles long on the winding road which passes Sellafield at Calder Bridge. The tailback was caused by the UKAEA policemen who guard the site staging a security exercise without warning. They decided to stop and search every vehicle entering the Sellafield site during the rush hour as the workforce turned up for the morning shift.

My car was stationary, just round a bend, and all I could do was to wait for someone to drive into the back of it – and a local district nurse did just that. I even felt sorry for her. I had nearly run into the back of the car in front of me. Had the nurse been driving any faster we could both have been killed. Mass evacuation has still not been provided for adequately at Sellafield. A single broken-down tractor can block parts of the A595, the so-called main trunk road where I sat waiting for the inevitable shunt. It is still little better than a country lane in places, nearly forty years after the pile fire pointed up the possible need for a fast escape route from Sellafield.

Not only was no one evacuated or told to stay indoors during the 1957 Sellafield fire but there was little restriction or safety instruction of any kind, beyond a somewhat belated decision to pour local milk away after it was found to be contaminated. The contamination came mainly from radioactive iodine, to which young children are particularly susceptible, as is now being shown once again in the aftermath of Chernobyl. Local farmers were compensated to the tune of £60,000 for their lost milk production and it was one of Brian Potts's anecdotes that the apparent milk yield doubled during the period of the ban. Canny people, the Cumbrian farmers!

The fire's effect on health and the environment is still not known for certain. We are not even sure how much radioactivity was released during the fire. Over the years the estimates have varied between some 21,500 curies and as much as 55,500 curies. For comparison, Sellafield discharged 3,400 curies of radioactivity during the whole of 1994. (The curie was the measure of radioactivity used by the nuclear industry until the 1980s, when it was replaced by the becquerel. For consistency, I will use the old measure throughout this book.)

There was also some initial doubt about where the material discharged during the fire was deposited. An early press release from the UKAEA spoke of light winds from the north-east blowing the radioactive plume out over the Irish Sea to the west. It was later established that the weather pattern was complex and changeable and that there were, in fact, two distinct plumes. The first carried material to the north-east and the second moved it down to the south-east over England and eventually, in low concentrations, over western Europe.

Despite these uncertainties, an initial assessment was made of the fire's effect on health by the UKAEA and by an expert group led by Sir Harold Himsworth, Chairman of the Medical Research Group (later the Medical Research Council). They came to the conclusion that it could be safely assumed that the public had suffered no harm as a result of the fire. Over the years that view has been refined several times as the effect of different forms of radiation on particular parts of the body has become better understood. It is now considered that the fire may lead – or have led – to 100 extra cancer deaths in the

UK and perhaps as many non-fatal effects again. We will never know for certain. The figure will be lost among the 140,000 or so cancer deaths which occur naturally in the UK every year.

To put this in perspective, thirty-three men died as a result of the horrific fire which started on 26 April 1986 at the Chernobyl nuclear power station in the Ukraine, then part of the USSR, and the UK's National Radiological Protection Board has estimated that around 30,000 fatal cancers will occur over the next forty years in the affected parts of Russia and western Europe as a result of that terrible event. A thousand times more radioactivity was released into the environment at Chernobyl than went up the Sellafield chimney during the 1957 fire. In Britain alone, the fall-out of nuclear materials from the Chernobyl accident may cause up to 100 deaths, as many as the Sellafield fire.

While it was nowhere near as serious as Chernobyl, the Sellafield fire was a very serious event by any normal standards of industrial safety – more serious in its effects than the accident at the Three Mile Island nuclear power station in the US in 1979, although that was handled so badly that 144,000 people fled from their homes, mainly without being asked to evacuate them. During the critical early stages of the Three Mile Island incident the nuclear authorities failed to set out the facts of the situation fully, openly and promptly, undermining the credibility of the later statements they issued.

This is precisely what had happened at Sellafield more than twenty years earlier. But the Three Mile Island accident was different in that it was the subject of extensive, often sensationalized media coverage, building on Doomsday scenarios which were presented as scientific fact by some of the anti-nuclear campaigners. This did not happen during the Sellafield fire. There was no anti-nuclear movement to speak of in Britain at that time – the Campaign for Nuclear Disarmament (CND) did not come into existence until 1958, a year after the Pile No. 1 fire occurred.

The chronology of the way the 1957 fire was handled by the Sellafield management is very revealing of the attitudes which prevailed on the site. It became known for certain that something untoward was going on inside Pile No. 1 at about two p.m. on Thursday 10 October, when dust from a routine air sampler half a mile away from the pile buildings was found to be abnormally radioactive, although there had been earlier suspicions. Health physics staff began taking additional air samples at a dozen or so points inside the site perimeter. Two and a half hours later it was discovered that some of the uranium in the centre of Pile No. 1 was red hot. Major releases of radioactivity took place around midnight that night and somewhere between nine a.m. and eleven a.m. on Friday 11 October.

It was not until noon that day, when the immediate danger was over, that the UKAEA's Chairman, Lord Plowden, was told. He immediately recognized the political implications of the event and informed the Prime Minister, Harold Macmillan. Somehow news of the fire did not reach the media until the flames had been put out – or at least nothing was published. This speaks volumes for the tight security on the Sellafield site at that time and for the more respectful attitude towards authority which existed among journalists forty years ago. From my experience, there would be no chance of keeping a major incident of that kind under wraps for so long today.

Sellafield's bosses seem to have treated the fire as though it was a purely local difficulty, not something which could have affected the whole country if it had got out of hand, as it certainly threatened to do. This uncommunicative attitude in times of crisis persisted throughout my career with BNFL – and almost certainly still exists. It is as though engineering and scientific virility demand that any problem should be solved before it is mentioned to anyone outside the select group of people immediately responsible for dealing with it.

Part of the reason for this secretive attitude lies in the

remoteness of the Sellafield site. It is still a hard two and a half hours' drive away from BNFL's headquarters at Risley and it took nearly twice as long to make the journey when the pile complex was being built and the fire occurred, before the M6 was built. Following the practice in the wartime services, most of the UKAEA drivers taking senior people between the two sites were women and several of them were still working for the UKAEA when I joined BNFL. People like Joan Smith, who often drove me up to Sellafield, had some interesting tales to tell of those pioneering days – the atrocious road conditions during the winters and the idiosyncrasies of some of the important men they chauffeured round the country.

Getting to and from London was even more difficult and it is still a dawn-to-dusk chore. In this situation it is easy for the senior management at Sellafield to see themselves as separate and unloved, ignored when things are going well and bitterly attacked by their colleagues and the media when things go wrong. And things will always go wrong on a site which has employed as many as 10,000 people and which handles materials which are highly dangerous, even in minute quantities.

It has also been a source of irritation among the Sellafield managers over the years that the important decisions about investment and labour relations have all been taken from the company's headquarters, more often than not influenced by pressures from the Government of the day. The men and women on the spot at Sellafield have then been left to cope with the consequences – or to pick up the pieces, as they have often seen it.

All of these factors have made the Sellafield staff rely on their own problem-solving ability and judgement, no matter what the company's rules and procedures tell them they must communicate to others. This rugged independence, as it has been called, has become the main feature of the site's culture, and in my view it all stems from the excessive secrecy which surrounded those early years at Sellafield as Britain rushed to get to the atomic bomb.

Self-reliance can be an admirable quality in senior managers in some industries, but in the nuclear industry decision-taking in splendid isolation can be very dangerous indeed. A second opinion, from people not having to face up to the stress and potential physical threat created by an emergency, would often have been useful. Offers of help were almost invariably regarded as interference – particularly when they came from people working at the company's headquarters at Risley. Time and again Sellafield left itself open to accusations of trying to cover up its mistakes, the most damaging accusation it can face. All too often the charge was justified.

Surprisingly, the Sellafield fire did nothing to deter the politicians of the day from pressing ahead with the development of civil nuclear power. A start had been made with the decision to build a nuclear power station, called Calder Hall, on the Sellafield site. It was fuelled by natural uranium metal encased in cladding made from magnesium oxide (providing the name Magnox for the fuel and for the stations which use it), cooled by carbon dioxide gas, in a matrix of graphite bricks which served as the moderator. This station was built primarily to produce plutonium for the weapons programme – a decision which was more than vindicated when the two plutonium production piles were shut down as a result of the fire in one of them twelve months after Calder Hall started up.

Queen Elizabeth II formally inaugurated Britain's civil nuclear power programme in October 1956 by pressing a switch which transferred electricity from Calder Hall to the national grid. With considerable patriotic fervour, the new station was hailed by the British press as the world's first full-scale nuclear power station. Rather less was made of the fact that it was also to produce weapons-grade plutonium, its prime purpose. Calder Hall is still operating today – and still producing plutonium for Britain's nuclear weapons programme (although rather less than it once did, with the easing of East-West tensions), as well as a small amount of electricity.

From the newspaper and radio accounts of the time and from what some of my older colleagues told me subsequently, there was a true sense of history in the making as guests and press correspondents from nearly forty countries gathered in west Cumbria for Calder Hall's opening ceremony. The flags were out, the crowds cheered and the band played on through the day. There seemed to be no limit to what this amazing new energy resource would achieve for mankind. Never mind about mankind – it was going to revitalize the ailing British economy and restore the country's prestige and influence abroad, at a time when they seemed to be slipping away. And that was far more important.

A form of nuclear euphoria swept over the country as otherwise sensible and suspicious people made ever more startling predictions about what was about to be achieved. Winston Churchill, in one of those resounding phrases of his, described nuclear power as 'a perennial fountain of world prosperity', and while I have failed to identify anyone who actually said that nuclear electricity would be 'too cheap to meter', that is certainly the impression which might have been gained from the early political speeches about prospects for the embryo civil nuclear power industry. Whether it was said or not, the 'too cheap to meter' quip has gone into the mythology of nuclear power.

At the Calder Hall opening ceremony R. A. ('Rab') Butler, then Lord Privy Seal, went as far as to speculate that by 1965 – nine years on from the time he was speaking – every new power station which was built would be atomic. And by 1975, he said, the total output of electricity from atomic stations would be greater than and possibly double the output of all the power stations then in existence. In the event, despite the drastic reduction in coal production in this country over the last couple of decades (which I deplore), coal – much of it now imported – still provides twice as much electricity as nuclear power. The costs of coal-fired and nuclear-powered electricity are broadly comparable. And, of course, we still have our electricity meters.

The Queen's speech at the opening of Calder Hall captured much of the excitement and pride with which the harnessing of atomic energy was greeted. There was also a little trepidation there too, which I find reassuring. 'So quickly have we learned to accept the pace of modern development that we have been in danger of losing our sense of wonder,' the Queen said. 'That sense has been dramatically restored by the advent of the atomic age. We have been made vividly aware that the physical world, in which the great adventure of human life is lived, is of a complexity which must inspire in us a sense of awe.' Those running the industry now would do well to remember that most people are still in awe of nuclear power – and rightly so. There is little margin for error or complacency.

People also share the sense of humility which the Queen expressed on that momentous day, a recognition that nuclear power holds tremendous possibilities for both good and evil. 'A grave responsibility is placed upon all of us to see that man adds as much to his stature by the application of this new power as he has by its discovery,' the Queen said. 'Future generations will judge us, above all else, by the way in which we use these limitless opportunities, which Providence has given us and to which we have unlocked the door.' I cannot help feeling that today's generation, if it thinks at all about what we did with the limitless opportunities of nuclear power, will not be very impressed.

Her Majesty went on to speak of Britain offering something new to the people of the undeveloped and less fortunate areas of the world, whom she believed would continue to look to Britain for assistance and example. 'For centuries past, visionary ideals and practical methods which have gone from our shores have opened up new ways of thought and modes of life for people in all parts of the world,' she said. 'It may well prove to have been the greatest of our contributions to human welfare that we led the way in demonstrating the peaceful uses of this new source of power.' Alas, because we chose the wrong systems we have followed rather than led on nuclear generation. We have had rather more success in pioneering some aspects of uranium treatment and fuel manufacture – and reprocessing at Sellafield.

The Queen's speech at the opening of Calder Hall seems pretty wide-eyed and not a little patronizing now, but at the time few wanted to challenge the promises held out by the nuclear scientists, or knew enough to do so. Perhaps all of the excitement is not so surprising. We were being told that in theory a single tonne of uranium would release as much energy as 3 million tonnes of coal if complete burn-up could be achieved with a fast-breeder reactor system – a concept which pulled us up short in amazement. Even in the first-generation reactors such as Calder Hall, with their relatively inefficient fuel burn-up systems, a tonne of uranium was expected to be equivalent to at least 10,000 tonnes of coal in energy terms.

And we were promised that it was not only electricity generation which was about to be revolutionized. Hardly an aspect of society was not going to be improved by the introduction of this new form of energy – industry, agriculture, medicine, communications, even fashion. Patents flooded out from the UKAEA, which was responsible for the whole of the nuclear industry in the late 1950s and early 1960s. Some of those promises have been kept, at least in part, and some have not.

The world does have nuclear-powered ships and submarines, although nuclear propulsion at sea is not as widespread as we were led to believe it was going to be forty years ago. Many of the applications of nuclear power in medicine and industry have also been developed in much the way we were told they would be, if more slowly than anticipated and sometimes, as in the use of X-rays, with scant regard for the dangers of radiation. Food preservation by irradiation is now allowed after decades of argument too, although there is no great customer enthusiasm for the products treated in this way. But some of the claims which were made about what nuclear power was going to do for us have a positively lunatic feel about them today.

We were told that the experts were working on the development of aircraft propelled by nuclear engines and immediately believed that cheap nuclear-powered holiday flights were just around the corner. Of course it never actually happened. The politicians and scientists were also discussing the possibility of nuclear-powered cars, lorries and trains – but they never happened either. And nothing at all came of what remains the nuclear industry's craziest idea, the irradiation of diamonds to make them change colour to blue, green or brown, despite the UKAEA's soft-sell assurances that the radioactivity which was used would decay to 'insignificance' within a few days.

Then as now, however, the prime non-military purpose of atomic energy was the generation of electricity and in that area the early confidence of Britain's nuclear scientists and the politicians bordered on arrogance. In February 1955, while the Windscale pile reactors were still apparently operating safely but before Calder Hall had even been commissioned, the Government produced a White Paper which set out a master plan for the construction of nuclear power stations over the following ten years and indicated possible developments over the decade after that. The Government had been persuaded, before a single kilowatt of nuclear electricity had reached the national grid, that nuclear power was such a certain winner, politically and economically, that it could launch into a major civil nuclear power programme.

In the space of five years Government policy on nuclear power turned cartwheels. In the 1955 White Paper the Government announced that the country was to have twelve nuclear power stations, based on the use of natural uranium fuel encased in cladding made from magnesium oxide. They were to have a combined capacity of about 2,000 megawatts. Two years later, in the wake of the Suez débâcle in the autumn of 1956, which led to fears of an oil famine, a revised programme was announced. Britain was now to have 6,000 megawatts of nuclear power capacity, saving an estimated 18 million tonnes of coal or its equivalent.

This threefold expansion of the original programme, which was not even under way, was to be achieved by the construction of nineteen Magnox power stations in England, Wales and Scotland and of a 150-megawatt nuclear station to be built in Northern Ireland, which would come into operation in 1963 or 1964. A nuclear power station in Northern Ireland – now there's a thought to conjure with. The Government even firmed up on what it intended to do in the second ten years of its nuclear power programme. The country was to have twelve more stations, providing another 1,500 to 2,000 megawatts of capacity.

In all, the United Kingdom was going to build no fewer than thirty-two nuclear power stations in a twenty-year period, and there were those in the UKAEA who believed that the final number would be much greater than that. It is a fortunate industry which gets indications of that level of support from Government – and the promise of substantial finance for research and development – before it has demonstrated that it can actually produce what it promises.

In 1955, the newly formed Central Electricity Generating Board (CEGB), responsible for the bulk supply of electricity to England and Wales, had a total installed capacity of just over 24,000 megawatts. So the new programme of up to 8,000 megawatts of nuclear capacity was a very substantial leap into the largely unknown.

As oil supply fears abated and coal industry production improved, a more detached examination of the potential of nuclear power took place. With barely a blush, the Government produced a further White Paper in June 1960, five years after the first one. This accepted that nuclear power would not become competitive with coal- and oil-fired electricity generation as early as had been expected. As a result a revised programme, providing for 5,000 megawatts of nuclear power to be installed by 1968, was brought in.

No fewer than five different consortia of industrial companies had been formed to build the thirty-two Magnox stations predicted by the Government in 1955. The programme was eventually completed in November 1971, consisting of only nine stations (plus the dual-purpose stations built at Sellafield and Chapelcross), with a total capacity of some 3,730 megawatts. All the stations were of a unique design and the fuel for them was varied too – and only three of the consortia were left in business. Nevertheless, the first civil nuclear power programme in Britain, based on the Magnox stations, was still a fairly substantial one and few doubted that nuclear power would eventually take over as the main fuel used in electricity generation.

Even as it busied itself designing nine different varieties of Magnox power stations and carrying out design studies for another nine totally different research reactors in the 1950s, the UKAEA managed to persuade the Government to allow it to press on with the design of several other types of 'commercial' nuclear reactor. At least one of these, they argued, could be expected to provide cheaper electricity than the Magnox stations, which represented a robust but not particularly efficient way of burning uranium. Once more the Government was told that the nuclear cornucopia was about to pour out its riches.

The most promising of the new reactor types was said to be the AGR, which the UKAEA's designers promised would burn up uranium more efficiently and produce higher operating temperatures than the Magnox reactors. This in turn would mean that more of the nuclear heat could be turned into electricity. The AGRs would be fuelled by enriched rather than natural uranium – that is, fuel containing a greater proportion of fissile U235 atoms than occurs naturally in uranium ore. Enriched fuels, or oxide fuels as they are sometimes called, are also used in the PWR, the boiling water reactor (BWR) and all of the reactor types built after the first-generation Magnox reactors and the Canadian CANDU reactor.

Some five tonnes of natural uranium has to be refined to obtain a tonne of enriched uranium. The extent of the enrichment needed in particular fuels varies with the requirements of different reactors, but the percentage of U235 present in AGR fuel is increased from the naturally occurring level of 0.7 per cent to between 2 and 3 per cent. Carry on the enrichment process long enough, taking the enrichment level up to around 90 per cent, and you end up with weapons-grade material. This explains the concern about countries such as Iraq obtaining enrichment technology, ostensibly for the purpose of developing civil nuclear power programmes.

Planning for a prototype AGR using enriched fuel began less than a year after the opening of Calder Hall and before the real Magnox programme got under way. Yet again Sellafield was chosen as the site where the first of this new generation of nuclear reactors would be tried and tested. The Windscale AGR (WAGR), affectionately known as 'Wagger', first supplied electricity to the national grid in February 1963 – but not much of it. WAGR's capacity was only twenty-eight megawatts, but the experience gained with it was thought to be enough to use the design as the basis of a second major civil nuclear power programme. After all, the Magnox programme had been launched on the back of far less experience.

'Wagger' had been operating for just over a year when the new programme was announced. The Government had decided that 5,000 megawatts of AGR capacity were to be brought into operation between 1970 and 1975. The WAGR, the golf-ball-shaped building often shown as an introduction to television programmes about Sellafield, usually accompanied by sepulchral music, was shut down in 1982 and is now being taken apart. It is providing invaluable reactor decommissioning experience.

In this second civil nuclear power programme a total of seven twin-reactor AGR stations were eventually built, five by the CEGB for England and Wales and two by the South of Scotland Electricity Board (SSEB). In the early 1960s the electricity generating industry decided that big was beautiful and the new stations were to be far bigger than anything built before – each station was to have two sets of 660 megawatts. This was a twentyfold sale-up of the prototype AGR at Sellafield.

The AGR construction programme was a disaster. Dungeness B, the first station to be started, took twenty years to build, instead of the three anticipated, and the others were between three and four years behind schedule. For some years they produced electricity for only 30 per cent of the available time and it is only since Nuclear Electricity was formed out of the CEGB that their performance has been improved to a highly respectable 75–80 per cent availability figure, which is among the best in the world. With only nuclear stations to worry about and ambitions for their companies to be privatized, minds within NE have been concentrated wonderfully on the task of improving the performance of the AGRs – somewhat late in the day perhaps, but no less welcome for that.

As if all the research and development work being devoted to the AGRs and research reactors was not enough during the 1960s, the UKAEA was also working on three other reactor types which they believed had commercial potential, two of which were eventually built as prototypes at Winfrith in Dorset. The first was the Dragon high-temperature reactor, an international project, which started up in 1964. The second was a 100-megawatt steam-generating heavy water reactor (SGHWR), which went into operation in 1968. Both reactors are now shut down. The third reactor type being worked on by the UKAEA was the fast-breeder reactor, which the reactor designers regarded as their ultimate goal.

The one reactor type which was not being developed by the UKAEA was the PWR – the reactor developed in the US and chosen by most other countries with a civil nuclear power programme. To the UKAEA's horror, in December 1973 the Chairman of the CEGB, Arthur Hawkins, someone I knew from his days as Chairman of the CEGB's Midlands Region and mine as Industrial Editor of the *Birmingham Post*, announced that the CEGB planned to follow the AGRs with no fewer than thirty-two PWRs designed by the American company Westinghouse over the next decade, each with 1,300 megawatts of capacity. Speaking to the Commons Select Committee on Science and Technology, Sir Arthur, as he became, dismissed the AGRs as 'a catastrophe we must not repeat' and the SGHWR as 'unproven and expensive, already an obsolete technology'.

Sir Arthur's proposal was roundly attacked by an assorted group of opponents – the Select Committee itself, trade unions concerned that an American reactor type would provide more jobs in the US than in Britain, the SSEB, which had always been fonder of the AGR than the CEGB and had also championed the cause of the SGHWR, a large section of the nuclear power industry and the media, and Friends of the Earth. In July 1974 the Labour Government of the day squashed the idea. Eric Varley, then Secretary of State for Energy, overruled Sir Arthur. He announced that the new programme would not be based on the AGR or the PWR but on the SGHWR, and that he was only prepared to authorize 4,000 megawatts of extra nuclear capacity, not the 41,000 megawatts Sir Arthur wanted.

Two years later, in August 1976, Sir John Hill, Chairman of the UKAEA, advised Tony Benn, who had taken over from Eric Varley at the Department of Energy in 1974, that the future domestic market for nuclear power stations no longer warranted the introduction of the SGHWR and none was built beyond the Winfrith prototype. Sir John continued to insist that one day the country would need a large nuclear programme and that something must be done to retain the industrial capability necessary to undertake a mixed programme of thermal and fast breeder reactors in, say, 1985. However, there was no large nuclear programme and the industrial capacity was largely dissipated.

Just one new reactor order was placed in the 1980s, when Lord Marshall, Chairman of the CEGB and a former Deputy Chairman of the UKAEA, managed to persuade the Thatcher Government to allow the CEGB to order a Westinghouse PWR, the Sizewell B power station in Suffolk, which was eventually commissioned by Nuclear Electric in 1994 and which has got off to a promising start. Lord Marshall had hoped that Sizewell B would be the first of a series of PWRs and that this time – for the first time – the country would benefit from series ordering of nuclear power stations.

The reactor which was eventually built at Sizewell was very much a British PWR, however, and not the off-the-shelf American reactor which had once been talked about, because of the extra layers of safety demanded by the Nuclear Installations Inspectorate. It remains to be seen whether there will be any more of them. The PWR programme planned by Nuclear Electric when it took over the CEGB's nuclear power responsibilities was put on hold for four years when the Government privatized electricity generation, to give the new investors in mainly coal-fired electricity generation who had bought shares in National Power and PowerGen a decent run for their money without increased competition.

The vision of Sir John Hill and enthusiasts such as the late Tom Marsham, a non-executive director of BNFL who was also Managing Director of the UKAEA's Northern Division, that one day the fast-breeder reactor would come into its inheritance now seems likely to be no more than that – a scientific dream. The theoretical attractions of the fast-breeders are obvious. The system uses fuel made from the plutonium and U238 recovered by reprocessing or, in the case of U238, left over from the enrichment process. The fast-breeder can be operated so that it not only generates electricity but also produces more plutonium, enough to provide both its own replacement in the reactor and more besides. Hence the term breeder.

It has been estimated that the uranium needed to fuel seven AGRs for ten years could fuel fast-breeder reactors with a comparable generating capacity for as long as 850 years. In the mid-1970s the UKAEA was talking of Britain having at least twenty commercial fast-breeders operating by the turn of the century and probably many more, and plutonium was said to be worth seven times its weight in gold. But this depended on the UKAEA persuading the Government and the electricity generating boards that it could scale up the prototype fast-breeders built at Dounreay and produce a reactor which had commercial prospects. This it failed to do. There are no commercial fast-breeders and none is contemplated. And it is difficult to say what plutonium is worth.

The Government's decision to stop pouring money into the fast-breeder project and to do little more than keep it ticking over was prompted by advice from John Guinness, the current Chairman of BNFL, when he was at the Department of Energy. I agreed with his advice at the time and still feel that it was right for the plug to be pulled on research which had been promising jam tomorrow for decades. But there is a certain irony in the fact that the advice came from Mr Guinness. In the absence of commercial fast-breeders the huge stockpiles of recovered U238 held by BNFL will continue to grow. They may come to be regarded as just another nuclear waste product rather than an energy resource – and the stocks of unused plutonium held by BNFL at Sellafield are in danger of being seen in the same light.

That throws into question whether it is now worth BNFL reprocessing spent fuel at all, or whether used fuel rods, containing a cocktail of plutonium, uranium and fission products, should simply be regarded as the waste products of nuclear electricity generation and dumped. There were few such doubts when I joined the nuclear industry twenty years ago. Reprocessing at Sellafield was all set for massive expansion.

Chapter Two

Reprocessing:

The World's Nuclear Dustbin

There were nearly two THORPs, not one, and they came within an ace of being built without any form of public inquiry, something which would be unthinkable today. Such was the apparent need for reprocessing twenty years ago, combined with the perception by politicians and scientists that the public were either not interested in what went on at Sellafield or were prepared to give their tacit support in the national interest. All that was changed by a brilliant newspaper campaign, sponsored by Friends of the Earth and supported by Tony Benn, together with an incident at Sellafield which the management chose to try to cover up.

Like the first nuclear power reactor, the first reprocessing plant in Britain was built at Sellafield and for precisely the same reason – the need to obtain plutonium for atomic weapons. There was just as much pressure on the pioneer nuclear scientists and engineers to build the military reprocessing plant, which came into operation in 1952, as there was to build the plutonium production piles on the same site. It was an equally significant scientific and engineering achievement, demonstrating for the first time on a full-scale production basis that plutonium and unused uranium could be separated and used in the generation of electricity as well as in the manufacture of bombs.

When a spent fuel rod leaves the reactor, where it will have been producing energy for up to seven years, it consists of 97 per cent unused uranium – mainly U238 but including what is left of the fissile U235 which was originally present. Between 0.1 per cent and 1 per cent is the plutonium which has been formed and between 2 and 3 per cent comprises fission products, the radioactive substances which have been regarded as the true wastes of the nuclear electricity generation process until now.

The purpose of reprocessing is to separate these three constituents, the first two of which – uranium and plutonium – were thought to have an important further use in new fuel. New fuel from old: reprocessing was seen in the early days of nuclear power as an alchemist's dream, to be applauded by anyone truly interested in the conservation of energy and natural resources.

There was an added incentive to press ahead with reprocessing at the start of the civil nuclear power programme in Britain, which does not apply to nearly the same extent now. The UK has no appreciable indigenous supplies of uranium ore. The main deposits outside the former Communist countries (which were not available forty years ago but most certainly are today) are in the US, Canada, Australia, South Africa and Namibia. With several countries pressing ahead with nuclear power programmes and others eager to do so, shortages of uranium – and high prices – seemed a distinct possibility in the 1950s. A process which would enable all, or nearly all, of the previously imported uranium (both the U238 and the U235) to be used for electricity generation, as well as the separated plutonium, had obvious attractions.

In the case of the early natural uranium fuel, the need for

reprocessing was also dictated by the way in which the fuel was stored after being taken out of the reactor prior to reprocessing. It was stored in water, which acted as a coolant and as a shield against direct radiation reaching members of the workforce. Unfortunately, the magnesium oxide metal used in the cans which held the fuel element corroded easily. Left in the storage ponds for a year or so, radioactive materials would start to leach out into the water of the storage ponds, which then had to be washed out into the Irish Sea. If there was a delay in reprocessing for any reason, as there was during the early 1970s, these discharges to the sea built up to levels which would not be acceptable today.

Magnox fuel did not have to be stored in water. It could have been held in a dry condition in purpose-built stores, as it is at one of Nuclear Electric's Magnox power stations, Wylfa in North Wales. This would have at least delayed the need for reprocessing. But water containment was an easier and cheaper technology to develop in a hurry and as the country thought it necessary to reprocess as much fuel as it could in those early years in order to build up a stockpile of plutonium the need for water storage was not really questioned. The spent fuel was – and is – transported from the power stations to Sellafield for reprocessing in water-filled containers too.

The pattern was set and to change it by building dry stores at the Magnox stations which do not have such facilities, by constructing further dry stores at Sellafield and changing over to dry transport flasks, or by drying the fuel out at Sellafield, would cost so much that it would have probably brought the Magnox nuclear electricity programme to an end by now. Because of the way it is transported and stored, Magnox fuel has to be reprocessed and this is now accepted by most of the anti-nuclear lobbyists.

The military reprocessing plant was shut down after it had operated for twelve years and replaced by a new plant sized to reprocess civil nuclear fuel as well as military materials. It was built at Sellafield in response to the Government's announcements of a major Magnox power station construction programme and designed to match the maximum reprocessing programme envisaged. That did not materialize and as a result the reprocessing plant, which came into service in 1964, had surplus capacity.

Despite being over thirty years old, it is still going strong and is expected to operate until well into the next century. In fact, it has to do so. If it fails, the Magnox stations will have to be shut down precipitately and, as the plant has a military as well as a civil function, the ability to separate plutonium for the weapons programme will also be lost, unless the new reprocessing plant, THORP, supposedly dedicated to the reprocessing of civil nuclear fuel, is brought into play – a strategy which would be bitterly opposed.

The old plant was extensively refurbished during the 1970s, but parts of it are now showing their age and in the end reprocessing could be the limiting factor on the life of the remaining Magnox reactors. BNFL is to take over all of the Magnox power stations as part of the privatization of Nuclear Electric and Scottish Nuclear and is already talking of extending the lives of these stations to well into the next century. To make that possible it will carry out a further substantial refurbishment of the Magnox reprocessing plant in 1997.

Although Magnox fuel reprocessing has not been without its problems, BNFL can be proud of what it has achieved. Even on the lowest projection of how long the Magnox stations will operate, the company will have reprocessed around 50,000 tonnes of spent fuel and about 25,000 tonnes of recovered fissile U235 will have been recycled by the end of the Magnox reprocessing programme. Some 70 per cent of all the fuel produced for the AGR stations built in Britain has been made from recycled U235, reducing the need for uranium imports and thereby defraying some of the costs of reprocessing.

More than sixty tonnes of plutonium will also have been

recovered by the end of the Magnox reprocessing programme and THORP is expected to yield another forty tonnes of plutonium in its first ten years of operation. It will all be sitting there at Sellafield, unless the concept of blending plutonium with uranium in a mixed oxide fuel (MOX) and burning it in conventional reactors (but not, for technical reasons, in the AGRs) is widely accepted.

The use of MOX is being promoted actively by BNFL and sufficient interest is being shown in it by some of the company's reprocessing customers for BNFL to have a 120 tonnes a year MOX fuel manufacturing plant under construction. Costing some £300 million, it is expected to be in operation by 1998. It would ease the perceived risk from terrorism if plutonium was returned to BNFL's customers as a mixed fuel, as the Royal Commission on Environmental Pollution recommended over twenty years ago. MOX fuel would have to be reprocessed again if the plutonium in it was to be extracted and that would be relatively easy to detect.

No one pretends that the use of MOX fuels will be sufficient to justify plutonium separation, although a recent study by the Organization for Economic Cooperation and Development indicated that MOX could be up to 30 per cent cheaper than conventional uranium fuel. Burning MOX fuel is seen by BNFL's customers more as a way of disposing of the plutonium which they own and which is perhaps an unwelcome responsibility.

In the late 1960s it was decided to use the spare capacity in the reprocessing plant built for Magnox fuel to reprocess oxide fuel from the AGR stations which were being built in the UK and from the PWRs and BWRs being constructed overseas. As it was still assumed that plutonium would be needed for the very substantial fast-breeder reactor programme which was envisaged, nobody then questioned that oxide fuel reprocessing was necessary. Radioactive materials are unlikely to leach through the stainless-steel cladding used for AGR fuel or the zircalloy used on PWR fuel for at least fifty years, so there was plenty of time to develop alternative methods of dealing with the spent fuel if this was thought necessary, but the possibility was not seriously examined.

The first attempt to reprocess oxide fuel involved the use of a so-called Head End plant built on to the old military reprocessing plant at Sellafield. In this the spent oxide fuel was chopped up into pieces and dissolved in boiling nitric acid before passing on for chemical separation in the new Magnox reprocessing plant. The Head End plant was completed in August 1969 and offered a cheaper way of reprocessing oxide fuel than would have been possible if a purpose-built plant had been designed and built.

In BNFL's first annual report, covering the year 1971–2, Sir John Hill, Chairman of both the UKAEA and BNFL (and my first Chairman), spoke with pride of the company's achievement in winning several overseas contracts for reprocessing oxide fuel in the combined Head End and Magnox reprocessing plants. The following year he reported that Sellafield had received spent fuel from Canada, Germany, Italy, Japan, Spain and Switzerland and that more overseas business was expected.

The Head End plant operated for only four years, reprocessing a total of ninety tonnes of spent oxide fuel. In September 1973 it had to be shut down when there was what was described as a small release of radioactivity into the operating area of the plant, contaminating thirty-five workers. As a result BNFL was left with some 350 tonnes of overseas fuel on its hands, which it was contractually committed to reprocess but which had nowhere to go.

For several years the company talked of refurbishing the Head End plant and reprocessing the stored overseas fuel in it, but finally the plant had to be written off. It is still there, awaiting decommissioning. The fuel is still there too. Unfortunately for BNFL, this overseas fuel, accepted for reprocessing at very low prices, will now have to go into THORP. Most of the original prices were negotiated up to some extent (but not as far as BNFL would have liked), a painful process which took over a decade. But one customer, a Spanish utility, refused to move at all from the strict contract terms. This leftover business from the Head End plant will cost BNFL a great deal of money – just how much will depend on how well THORP operates.

Despite the Head End incident, BNFL was determined to reprocess oxide fuels, which it saw as an extremely profitable activity. It was also becoming obvious that the UK nuclear programme was not going to expand as quickly as had once been thought. As it was Government policy that BNFL should set out to capture overseas business – that was the main reason the company was formed – BNFL had no reason to think that Government approval for the construction of the new reprocessing plant or plants needed to carry out this overseas business would be withheld.

The original plan was to build a THORP with a nominal capacity of 2,000 tonnes a year. This was then changed to a proposal to build two THORPs, each with a capacity of 1,000 tonnes a year, one dedicated to the reprocessing of British fuel from the AGRs and the other to overseas fuel. At 2,000 tonnes, the THORP or THORPs would have had nearly twice as much capacity as the THORP plant which was actually built. By 1975 a single THORP, of much the size we have today, had been settled upon, although it was still felt likely that a second THORP would be built at some time in the future. Many of the overseas customers, particularly the Japanese, preferred the idea of having their fuel reprocessed alongside fuel from British reactors in one plant. They recognized early on that a dedicated overseas plant might not be acceptable politically.

The THORP project was known about fairly widely and seemed to be accepted. David Fishlock of the *Financial Times* had written about THORP's prospects in positive terms, emphasizing its considerable export-earning potential, and there were supportive pieces in several other newspapers. But some people did not see THORP in the same light, and just before I joined BNFL they set out to scupper the embryo project.

During the early morning of Tuesday 21 October 1975, Helen, my daughter, came into the bedroom and handed over a copy of the *Daily Mirror*, explaining that her mother thought I ought to read it right away. I took the paper from her and glanced at the front page headline. 'Windscale – the World's Nuclear Dustbin', it read. I started working for BNFL that day, although I was still employed by the *FT* and had a fortnight to go before my resignation notice ran out.

I rang Con Allday, who was furious about the *Mirror* story, and then spoke at length to Brian Potts, who was the company's only full-time press officer. From what Brian told me, it was obvious that BNFL had been wrong-footed by an extremely clever anti-nuclear operator. A *Mirror* reporter had called BNFL about the paper's 'exclusive' front-page story little more than an hour before its first edition was printed, leaving the company with no time to work up a decent reply. Shortly afterwards the Press Association (PA), serving most of the national and regional papers in the country, had rung Brian Potts as well, following the 'dustbin' line taken by the *Mirror*. The *Mirror* and PA had taken an old story, the export-success piece written by David Fishlock and others, and turned it on its head. What David saw as a business success, the *Mirror* saw as a public disgrace.

The by-line on the *Mirror* story was that of Stanley Bonnet, which was odd in itself. Stanley was the paper's Education Correspondent and the *Mirror*'s Science Editor, Ronnie Bedford, usually wrote about nuclear power. Despite having Stanley Bonnet's by-line, the 'dustbin' story was in fact worked up by an industrial journalist, Bryn Jones, who had been briefed by Walt Patterson, the main anti-nuclear spokesman of Friends of the Earth. Bryn later became a full-time campaigner, first with Greenpeace and later with the environmental group formed by Anita Roddick, of The Body Shop fame.

The 'World's Nuclear Dustbin' story was the most blatant example of a reporter using his own newspaper to pursue a personal crusade that I have met. Unfortunately, it was also a splendid piece of campaigning journalism, with a truly memorable headline. The 'nuclear dustbin' tag has stuck to Sellafield ever since the *Mirror* first ran it, despite my efforts to kill it off and turn its title into that of the world's nuclear laundry, a more accurate description of what it does with spent fuel. I saw the dustbin reference used in newspapers and on television as recently as 1995 and will be surprised if it is ever buried.

Not only did the *Daily Mirror* bounce BNFL, it had lined up Tony Benn's support in advance. As soon as the story was printed, the Secretary of State for Energy welcomed the *Mirror's* initiative and called for a wide-ranging public debate on overseas reprocessing.

My first task was to decide what was to be done about the *Daily Mirror*. The second was what, if anything, should be done about Tony Benn. My advice to Con Allday, who was tempted to have a public row with Mr Benn over his support for the *Daily Mirror*, was for him to keep his head down and say nothing, while Brian Potts and I concentrated on limiting the damage caused by the *Mirror* piece.

I told Brian and his boss, Gordon Williams, BNFL's publicity manager, who was busy promoting the company's commercial interests, that we had to think positively and try to turn what had happened to our advantage. However unfortunate the *Mirror* story might seem, there was no denying that it had aroused the public's interest in Sellafield and reprocessing. BNFL must satisfy that interest. While Con Allday should stay in the background, the company must raise its profile. On my instructions, Brian invited Fleet Street to send reporters up to Sellafield to see reprocessing for themselves – a bit risky as I had not been there myself and did not know whether the journalists would come back reassured or terrified.

We also invited the press to witness spent fuel arriving from overseas at Barrow-in-Furness, where BNFL still has its shipping terminal. Among those who turned up for this visit was Stanley Bonnet of the *Daily Mirror.* We spent several days together at Barrow, awaiting the arrival of a ship carrying fuel from Italy. Of all things, the ship developed engine trouble and struggled into port several days late. Stanley and I drank quite a few Scotches as he teased me that he was working up a speculative piece that the ship had sunk. Stanley did not write that story. In fact, he did not write very much at all and gradually the impact of the 'dustbin' story began to fade. As usual on these occasions, because the *Daily Mirror* was intent on claiming the story as an exclusive, the other tabloids largely ignored it or rallied to BNFL's defence.

This left Tony Benn and Parliament. At that time, there was little opposition to nuclear power within the two main political parties, although the Liberals were starting to express concern about its environmental effects. Despite the Government's apparent support, however, a few back-bench Labour MPs attacked BNFL's plans for overseas reprocessing. It was obvious that they were being briefed by Friends of the Earth. I asked Brian Potts and Gordon Williams what information BNFL had which could be sent out to MPs quickly. No suitable material existed. BNFL had concentrated its early public relations effort on the production of scientific and commercial films and brochures.

I set to and produced a note explaining what reprocessing was, why it was necessary and how valuable the overseas business was expected to be, based on a series of interviews which I conducted internally, and shot it off to all Members of Parliament, including Tony Benn. From the response to that first letter to MPs, it was possible for me to start to identify who was in favour of nuclear power, who was against it and who was undecided or uninterested. BNFL had made no such analysis previously. In 1975 the company did not even know where the young MP for Whitehaven (now Copeland), Dr John (Jack) Cunningham, stood on nuclear power, even though Sellafield was in his constituency and he was a junior minister at the Department of Energy, working for Tony Benn.

Con Allday had never met Jack Cunningham, but that was soon remedied. One evening in early December 1975 the three of us shared an enjoyable working dinner at the Boulestin in London, and Con and I learned to our considerable relief that we had the support of the local MP. From that night Jack did what he could to help us counter the *Mirror* story, although he obviously had to be careful not to do anything which might suggest a rift between him and Tony Benn.

I also renewed my acquaintance with Bernard Ingham, a former Labour Correspondent with the *Guardian* whom I knew from my days with the *Financial Times*. Bernard was Director of Information at the Department of Energy and was having his own problems with Tony Benn at the time. Bernard introduced me to Jean Caines, the Press Officer responsible for nuclear power, who was as new to the subject as I was.

The three of us discussed what had to be done to satisfy Tony Benn's determination to have his wide-ranging public debate about overseas reprocessing. I had already set up a series of debates and lectures in church halls and town halls throughout west Cumbria, where it seemed to me that people had a legitimate interest in the issue, but Bernard told me that this would not satisfy his Secretary of State.

In politics, little is believed to have happened unless it has taken place in London. I think it was Bernard who came up with the idea of BNFL organizing – and paying for – a set-piece debate at Church House, Westminster. The Church House debate, which Tony Benn introduced, was held on Thursday 16 January 1976 and lasted all day. The debate was chaired by Sir George Porter and the BNFL speakers were Con Allday and Peter Mummery, the general manager responsible for Sellafield. Walt Patterson and a Dr Paul Smoker represented those opposed to overseas reprocessing.

At one stage Dr Smoker accused BNFL and the Department

of Energy of 'news management' in organizing the discussion, and of course he was right. Nevertheless, I thought this was a bit thick after the way the *Daily Mirror*'s 'dustbin' coverage had been managed by Friends of the Earth. I took some encouragement from the remark, however. BNFL's fight back was having an effect on the opposition.

There was a great deal of blood-letting and rhetoric at Church House that day and at the end of it those supporting reprocessing and those opposing it remained poles apart. But it seemed to do the trick as far as Tony Benn was concerned. On 12 March 1976 he announced that the Government had decided that BNFL might take on further reprocessing work for overseas customers, subject to the negotiation of satisfactory terms, including the option to return radioactive waste to the country of origin. This statement took most of the steam out of the debate.

Three months later, BNFL applied to Cumbria County Council for outline planning permission to carry out improvements to the Magnox reprocessing facilities at Sellafield (which the Council was hardly likely to refuse) and to build THORP. The two projects were deliberately linked. The Council would not be rushed into taking a quick decision, however. At a public meeting held at Whitehaven Civic Hall on 29 September, Peter Mummery warned the Council that protracted delay in granting approval for THORP 'despite the Government's support of this business' could damage BNFL's prospects of obtaining valuable contracts from overseas. Time was to prove him right, but the Council was not prepared to let him steamroller the application through.

At the beginning of November the Council's town and country planning committee announced that although it was 'minded to approve the application', it was referring the matter to the Department of the Environment as it involved a departure from a fundamental provision of the County Development Plan. This was clearly a device to pass the decision on to the Government – and there was nothing BNFL could do about it.

According to my Whitehall sources at that time, the matter was immediately taken to the full Cabinet, which was all set to approve THORP quickly. I was led to believe that BNFL would get a favourable decision as long as a few extra questions were answered, each of a relatively minor nature. All that changed early in December, when BNFL was accused of covering up a leak of radioactive water from an old concrete silo containing the magnesium oxide cladding removed from spent Magnox fuel before it is reprocessed. Magnox cladding has to be kept under water because of the danger of spontaneous combustion. The Sellafield management had stumbled upon the problem two months earlier, on 10 October 1976, when it carried out a routine radiation survey of the completed excavations for a new silo which it intended to build next to the old one.

Radiation was detected in one corner of the excavation, but no one outside the factory was told about it. A more detailed survey was carried out a week later and it became apparent that the contamination arose from what I was later to describe as a seepage of water through the concrete wall of the old silo, some fifteen feet below the ground. Some seepage! Radioactive water was leaking at the rate of over 100 gallons a day. The silo had been built in 1964 with a capacity of 70,000 gallons. It was therefore more than likely that tens of thousands of gallons of contaminated water had already soaked into the ground.

On 22 October Sellafield informed regional officials of the Nuclear Installations Inspectorate of the event and their counterparts at the Department of the Environment were told on 27 October. But nobody bothered to tell anyone at the company's headquarters. It has to be assumed that the Sellafield management had either decided not to rock the boat while THORP was being discussed by the Cabinet and Cumbria County Council or thought that the incident was too small to matter, a view which seems to have been accepted by the regulatory authorities.

Until 1994, when BNFL started to empty it, the B38 silo was still being used, forgotten by the politicians and journalists who were once so concerned about it. When I last checked, in mid-1995, the emptying programme was said to be going well, but all the solid material had not been taken out and the contaminated water in the silo had still not been totally drained. Nor had the soil beneath the silo been removed, although BNFL was able to assure me that the radioactive water which contaminated it was 'fixed' and was not moving, as liquids tend to do, towards the sea.

Early in December, nearly two months after the B38 silo problem was first identified at Sellafield, Jack Cunningham rang me to ask what I knew about a leak at Sellafield. He had been told about it by Denis Howell, one of his MP colleagues, better known for refereeing football matches and making rain than for any interest in nuclear power, who had picked up a rumour circulating in the Commons. I told Jack that I doubted whether the rumour could be true as I knew nothing about it, but I would check. It was only too true, of course. Tony Benn was told about the incident on 8 December and BNFL made a public statement the following day.

The Secretary of State was furious with Con Allday for not telling him about the leak earlier and their relationship was strained from then on. Con was too loyal to the Sellafield management to admit to Tony Benn that he had not been told either. Peter Mummery was moved out of Sellafield within six months and became Director of Health and Safety at BNFL's headquarters at Risley. I have to say that in later years no one could have been more suspicious about what his former colleagues at Sellafield might be covering up than he was. I invariably found Peter's advice on the importance of particular incidents at Sellafield invaluable.

Within days of being told about the silo leak Tony Benn issued an edict that in future any nuclear incident, 'however apparently trivial', had to be reported to him. He would then decide whether to make the matter public. I persuaded Con Allday that this would leave the company too vulnerable to the views of the Secretary of State on whether an incident was important or not and to him choosing the timing of any subsequent public announcement. We agreed that the company itself would issue a press release about every event reported to Tony Benn and the Department of Energy. BNFL still issues such press releases, although the reporting criteria now allow the more trivial incidents to be ignored.

A more serious consequence of the discovery of the B38 silo leak was that any chance BNFL had of avoiding a public inquiry vanished. On 22 December 1976 Peter Shore, the Secretary of State for the Environment, announced that BNFL would be invited to submit a separate application for the oxide reprocessing plant proposal, detached from its plans to reinforce Magnox reprocessing. This application would then be called in for public inquiry. The application was resubmitted by BNFL on 1 March 1977 and the inquiry opened on 14 June 1977.

As Peter Mummery had predicted, the inevitable delay caused by the inquiry led to BNFL losing business, at least in part. The French nuclear fuel company, Compagnie Générale des Matières Nucléaires (COGEMA), had previously shown little or no interest in reprocessing foreign fuel. Following a reorganization, however, COGEMA started talking to BNFL's potential overseas customers, particularly the Japanese. BNFL had to agree to split the Japanese business with the French in roughly equal proportions and the French also took the lion's share of the European business. Con Allday was relieved to hang on to as much overseas business as he did.

It can be argued that the Sellafield management's cover-up of the B38 silo leak cost BNFL overseas earnings of up to £6,000 million, but that is too simplistic a view. Announcing the leak when it was first discovered might also have led to a public inquiry and it is probable that the new head of

COGEMA, Georges Besse, would have stepped in at some stage anyway. COGEMA opened its version of THORP, the UP2 oxide fuel reprocessing plant at Cap La Hague, two years before THORP came into operation.

The so-called Windscale Inquiry was conducted by Mr Justice Parker. Held at Whitehaven Civic Hall, it lasted 100 days, closing on Friday 4 November 1977, and I was there for most of the time, briefing journalists. The inquiry inspector reported on 26 January 1978 and recommended approval for the construction of THORP. He did so in remarkably lucid and unequivocal terms and in language which could readily be understood by a lay readership. I know that Tony Benn had expected the report to be more ambivalent, leaving scope for the Government to order the THORP project to be delayed or abandoned.

Based on the evidence and assumptions placed before him, I believe that Mr Justice Parker was right to recommend that THORP be given the go-ahead and that the Callaghan Government of the day, supported by the Conservative opposition, was right to accept his recommendation. Unfortunately, many of those assumptions, honestly made and based on a policy which appeared to make sense, have been shown to be false. The case for THORP is by no means as strong as it appeared to be two decades ago.

At the time of the inquiry it was still assumed that there would be a very substantial expansion of nuclear power in the UK, even by witnesses appearing on behalf of THORP's opponents. Nuclear euphoria had not yet come to an end. The Department of Energy was forecasting that the nuclear power industry would have to treble its capacity by the year 2000.

Translated into a power station building programme, this pointed to a need for an additional eight nuclear stations being built by the year 2000, each of them with 1,250 megawatts of capacity. All of the stations were expected to produce spent oxide fuel which would be reprocessed alongside the fuel from the existing AGR stations. In fact, only one new station, the 1,200 megawatt Sizewell B PWR station, was brought into operation during that period – and Nuclear Electric has not committed itself to having any of the fuel from that station reprocessed.

Indeed, the UK nuclear electricity generating boards, whose predecessors, the CEGB and SSEB, had expressed themselves as staunch supporters of THORP at the time of the Windscale Inquiry, took eighteen years to make a firm contractual commitment to put any fuel through the plant – if indeed the commitment made by them in 1995, just before they learned that they were to be privatized, is firm.

Because of the early declarations of support by the CEGB and the SSEB, and the amount of fuel expected to come out of the AGR power stations which were apparently to be built, THORP was designed with a nominal capacity of 12,000 tonnes over a ten-year period, with the reprocessing rate building up gradually. Behaving extremely prudently, or so it seemed at the time, BNFL decided that the plant should actually be called on to reprocess only 6,000 tonnes of spent fuel over the first decade of its operation. This appeared to provide plenty of insurance against breakdowns and any other problems which might arise to affect production. It also decided that the cost of building THORP should be recovered over the first decade of the plant's operation. BNFL's original pricing policy for THORP was based on these apparently conservative assumptions.

But during the course of the design and construction programme it became apparent that the cost of reprocessing in THORP would be considerably higher than had been anticipated when contracts were signed with overseas customers, some of them before THORP had even received planning permission. The cost increase was partly the result of design and construction delays and partly the effect of THORP reprocessing having to bear its share of a massively expensive environmental clean-up programme which had simply not been anticipated or accounted for.

BNFL's overseas customers became increasingly restless as they were given the bad news about THORP costs by Jeff Tindle, the senior salesman responsible for THORP, who seemed to be going across to Japan and the Continent every few months at one stage. Under the terms of their cost plus contracts, overseas customers were required to provide stage payments as the massively expensive plant was built, as well as a 20 per cent profit margin for BNFL. This saved BNFL millions of pounds in interest payments, which would otherwise have had to be paid on capital expenditure borrowings.

In order to placate its overseas customers, BNFL announced in the late 1980s that THORP was to be treated as though it had a working capacity over ten years of 7,000 tonnes, rather than 6,000 tonnes. With THORP's costs now spread over a bigger throughput, customers could obtain some of the benefit if they took up the extra capacity pro rata to their original contractual commitment. They would pay a lower average price for this total tonnage, reducing the original 20 per cent mark-up. BNFL also began to sell capacity in the second ten years of THORP (the so-called post-baseload business) at prices substantially lower than in the first ten years. These pricing manoeuvres went down well with the overseas customers, but they also reduced the anticipated profitability of THORP.

By increasing the intended throughput of THORP in its first ten years from 6,000 to 7,000 tonnes, BNFL also ate into the margin it had built into its calculations of how well THORP would need to operate if it was to be successful financially. Instead of a throughput averaging 600 tonnes a year it now needed to average 700 tonnes, which looked reasonably conservative at the time the change was made. Now I am not so sure. In its first year of operation, THORP's throughput was less than thirty tonnes and although Neville Chamberlain, BNFL's Chief Executive, felt able to say in the 1993–4 annual report that 'the two-year build-up to full production is now proceeding well' others were getting worried.

I sought clarification of the THORP throughput situation in mid-1995. I asked BNFL what Neville Chamberlain meant by 'full production' given that THORP now needed to average over 770 tonnes a year with nine years of its first decade to go. 'THORP will reprocess 7,000 tonnes of fuel during the first ten years of operation,' BNFL stated categorically. 'The plant is still undergoing commissioning and this task is progressing well. Because of the nature of the plant, the annual reprocessing figure is not really relevant, as this will obviously vary year by year depending upon operational conditions. What is important is that 7,000 tonnes of fuel are reprocessed during the baseload period. THORP management are confident this target will be achieved.'

Although the annual throughput figure is apparently irrelevant, Neville Chamberlain felt it necessary to provide a new figure to show that THORP was making progress in BNFL's 1994–5 annual report. 'During the financial year, the active commissioning and start-up of the THORP facilities have proceeded steadily, with a modest sixty-five tonnes of fuel being sheared and dissolved,' he said. According to Neville Chamberlain this was a substantial achievement, given the huge scale and engineering complexity of the plant, but I am not sure where that leaves the THORP commissioning team in relation to their Chief Executive's target of a two-year build-up to full production. I will read the 1995–6 report with interest.

Apart from the increase from 6,000 to 7,000 tonnes, there was another substantial change in the basis on which THORP had been described at the Windscale Inquiry and subsequently built, costed and marketed. The intention expressed at the inquiry was that THORP's capacity would be taken up by the UK generating boards and overseas customers on a fifty-fifty basis. That balance has been steadily eroded, to the extent that overseas fuel now accounts for 70 per cent of the loading of the plant. It would have been far more difficult for BNFL to obtain planning permission for THORP if that had been known at the outset. The argument that THORP would turn Britain into the 'World's Nuclear Dustbin' would have been brought into far greater play, possibly ending the plant's chances of being built.

Because so many of the parameters associated with the loading and costing of the plant had changed since approval for it was given, a case could obviously be made for the overall economics of THORP to be re-examined before it was allowed to start up. In 1993 Tom Burke, who as Director of Friends of the Earth had been one of the leaders of the original anti-THORP campaign nearly twenty years earlier, managed to persuade the Government that it should carry out just such a last-minute appraisal.

By then Tom had been an adviser to the Department of the Environment for several years – and his advice was that THORP, built and ready to go, would prove uneconomic for the country as a whole, whatever it did for BNFL's profits. Supported by economists sympathetic to the anti-nuclear cause, he managed to convince not only ministers at the Department of the Environment but Treasury officials that there might be something in what he said.

THORP had been virtually completed in September 1992 when I first heard that we had a problem over the commissioning of the plant. Sellafield, keeping its own counsel as usual, had known for two months that there was a potential difficulty. In July, officials of HM Inspectorate of Pollution and of the Ministry of Agriculture, Fisheries and Food had given the Sellafield management a revised timetable for agreeing the necessary environmental authorizations which had to be met if THORP was to start up as planned on 1 January 1993.

The Sellafield representatives at that July meeting were also told that there would be a public consultation on the draft authorizations which would start on 17 August 1992 and last for eight weeks and that there might be a public hearing, something which would inevitably delay the start-up of THORP. They still did not feel it necessary to warn anyone at Risley. The first intimation I had that all was not well came from one of my political liaison people at Risley, not from Sellafield.

He had learned from a contact at the Department of Energy that the Minister for Environmental Protection at the Department of the Environment, David MacLean, was taking a personal interest in the THORP issue. He was also told that some of Mr MacLean's officials were advocating that there should be a public hearing before THORP was allowed to start up. Unlike Sellafield, I took the matter seriously.

The Department had received over 12,000 letters demanding a full-scale public inquiry, prompted by Greenpeace. Such an inquiry would have delayed THORP for several years and, because of the uncertainty this would have created in the minds of BNFL's customers, it might never have operated. I was aware of Greenpeace's letter campaign, and later encouraged BNFL's unions to undertake a similar campaign supporting THORP. It was all so predictable that I could not see it unnerving a Government which was supposed to be firmly committed to reprocessing at Sellafield. It seemed impossible to me that the Government would stop THORP at such a late stage, with thousands of tonnes of UK and foreign fuel sitting in its storage ponds awaiting reprocessing.

I was concerned, however, when I learned that in addition to Tom Burke's involvement, a team from Greenpeace was to meet Treasury officials on 30 September. At that meeting the Treasury representatives were presented with a critical report on the financial viability of THORP prepared by Gordon MacKerron, from the Science Policy Research Unit at Sussex University, a known critic of THORP economics, and it was said that they had been impressed.

While Lord Melchett, the Executive Director of Greenpeace UK, and his team were at the Treasury, I was taking part in a crisis meeting at BNFL's Sella Park guest house, close to Sellafield. The meeting was chaired by John Guinness, the relatively new Chairman of BNFL, who had joined the company when the Department of Energy, where he was acting Permanent Secretary, was disbanded. Those present in addition to the Chairman were Neville Chamberlain, two other main board directors, Gregg Butler and Ken Jackson (who was then responsible for THORP), Alvin Shuttleworth, BNFL's Legal Director, and myself.

It did not take long for those round the table to realize that the Chairman intended to take the lead in any campaign BNFL decided to mount in defence of THORP. That was his prerogative, of course. John Guinness immediately announced that he would take personal responsibility for liaison with influential politicians and senior DTI and other Government officials, either directly or via Sir Gordon Reece, whom he told us he intended to appoint as a political consultant to BNFL, specifically to deal with the THORP start-up issue.

I challenged the need for this appointment, on the grounds that the company already had two consultants who were close to the Government and to the Conservative Party, Sir Bernard Ingham and Geoffrey Tucker, who were both fully up to speed on nuclear affairs. I could see no reason to take on a third consultant, particularly someone who had no special knowledge of the nuclear industry. The reason Mr Guinness gave for employing Sir Gordon Reece was that he was close to Michael Howard, then Secretary of State for the Environment. I already knew that David MacLean, the Environment Minister, was supporting a delayed start-up for THORP while some of the issues raised by Tom Burke within the Department were argued out. So it made sense to go round the corner to Mr MacLean's boss if that was possible, although I believed that Sir Bernard and Mr Tucker both knew Michael Howard as well as Sir Gordon did.

I met Sir Gordon Reece only twice – once at the Conservative Party conference, where he was engaged as a consultant by the Chairman, and once when I happened to be in BNFL's London office when he was there seeing Mr Guinness. He is clearly an excellent political lobbyist, but my suspicion that Sir Gordon knew very little about nuclear power was confirmed on both occasions. In fact one of my first tasks was to brief Sir Gordon and the 'bullet points' in favour of THORP which I produced for him in a hurry became the main source material for the campaign literature produced by BNFL later. Ironically, there was a Cabinet reshuffle shortly after Sir Gordon was appointed and Michael Howard left Environment to become Home Secretary, to be succeeded by John Gummer.

The role of David MacLean, who had succeeded Willie Whitelaw as the Member of Parliament for Penrith and the Border, is interesting. Despite being a Cumbrian MP, he refused to discuss his position with anyone from BNFL or Sellafield, either from the management or the trade unions. As the weeks went by, I found myself having to rely on one of his political opponents, Dale Campbell-Savours, the Labour MP for the neighbouring constituency of Workington, to act as an intermediary in order to counter the arguments Mr MacLean was receiving from Tom Burke – a ludicrous situation.

At first, however, I was forbidden by Mr Guinness to talk to anyone about the problems we were having with THORP. I wanted to bring Lord Whitelaw, Sir Bernard Ingham and Geoffrey Tucker into play within the Conservative Party and to brief Jack Cunningham, Dale Campbell-Savours and one of BNFL's Labour Party consultants, Ken Woolmer, as well as influential supporters within industry and the trade unions. I also could not understand why Mr Guinness did not take the matter directly to Michael Heseltine, BNFL's shareholder on behalf of Government, who was Michael Howard's Cabinet counterpart.

Mr Guinness said that he preferred to deal with Tim Eggar,

the minister responsible for Energy at the DTI, and to discuss the affair informally with Lord Wakeham, who had so recently appointed him Chairman of BNFL. Mr Guinness informed the BNFL board that he had ready access to Lord Wakeham, who was a relative of his. I asked BNFL to tell me more about this relationship while I was researching this book and was told, somewhat obscurely, that 'their respective wives are connected by marriage'.

Mr Guinness clearly felt at first that BNFL could win the argument over THORP in reasonable time by working within the Whitehall system, on which he is of course an expert. He was content for the future of his company's flagship project to be decided by his old friends the Whitehall warriors, as Lord Whitelaw once described the Civil Service mandarins who so delight in intellectual jousting over what are often primarily political issues – as the start-up of THORP most certainly was. I think it is an apt description.

Tom Burke, a known opponent of THORP of twenty years' standing, was allowed in on the Whitehall discussions as an adviser to the Department of the Environment – and made most of the running at these discussions – without BNFL raising any objection. I would have screamed foul, loudly and publicly. BNFL's detailed financial, environmental and social arguments for the operation of THORP were represented at second-hand by an official from the Department of Trade and Industry. The official, who had worked with Mr Guinness on the electricity privatization at the Department of Energy and was highly rated by him, briefed himself thoroughly, bombarding my staff with hundreds of questions, but we had no way of judging how well he performed at the Whitehall meetings.

BNFL lost several weeks of valuable time at the start of 1993 which should have been used to launch a high-profile and very public campaign in support of THORP, in an attempt to nip in the bud the last-minute effort by environmentalists to stop the plant operating. The campaign approach had to be adopted in the end, as the Whitehall discussions dragged on throughout 1993, causing a delay which will cost BNFL more than £100 million over the operating lifetime of the plant.

Every major Government department became involved in the Whitehall appraisal of THORP's overall economics, its effect on the finances of BNFL and its customers and the cost of its environmental impact. BNFL produced some very impressive figures to show that the THORP project was a profitable one for BNFL. Even assuming the worst possible scenario, BNFL estimated that THORP would make a profit of at least £500 million during its first ten years of operation. The company also claimed that it had secured advance orders worth £9,000 million, over half of which were from overseas customers, and expected to attract at least a further £2,500 million in foreign earnings.

THORP's opponents refused to accept these figures and argued that the real issue was not whether BNFL would make a profit out of the new plant but whether the overall economics of the project were good for Britain. From the reports we were getting from the Whitehall meetings, it was obvious that one of the Treasury economists was by no means convinced that was the case. I argued that BNFL needed an independent appraisal of THORP's economics, an argument that quickly took hold. Somewhat to my surprise, the task was given to the accountancy firm of Touche Ross, whose senior partner, John Roques, is also a non-executive director of BNFL – an interest which was publicly declared. There were concerns that this might be used by opponents to dispute the independence of the appraisal, but this did not happen to any real extent.

The Touche Ross study took several months to complete, despite an immense effort by BNFL staff to provide the reams of financial information required for it. This shows how complicated the THORP business scenario had become and I have to say that I began to get a little nervous about what

Touche Ross would eventually conclude – and I was not the only BNFL director who was getting worried. Eventually, Touche Ross produced its findings, to sighs of relief at BNFL. The economic benefit to Britain of operating THORP for its first ten years would be £950 million, according to Touche Ross, and if THORP was abandoned some £1,260 million of overseas revenue would be lost.

The Touche Ross exercise undoubtedly helped THORP's cause, although its findings were naturally attacked by the plant's opponents, who claimed that the operation of THORP would lead to an overall cost to the UK economy of at least £600 million. Whether Touche Ross would come to the same favourable conclusion about the economics of THORP as it did in 1993 if it carried out the appraisal again today is open to question, as the figures fed into its study by BNFL – and into the Whitehall exercise – have turned out to be incorrect in several important respects.

That is not a criticism of the company, which could only tell those conducting the two studies what it believed the situation to be at that time, on the basis of statements of intent by its UK customers. But as it was still negotiating with Nuclear Electric and Scottish Nuclear right through to 1995, it was stretching a point to say that it had 'secured' UK orders in 1993 and the final 30 per cent represented by the UK business eventually agreed is hardly 'nearly half'.

It is also now apparent that BNFL did not secure the prices for THORP reprocessing from Nuclear Electric and Scottish Nuclear which it had expected to get in 1993. Even as the Whitehall and Touche Ross appraisals were going on NE and SN were negotiating their prices down. From statements made by the two utilities when they finally signed their THORP contracts in 1995, they probably achieved a reduction of at least 10 per cent on the figures BNFL had been feeding into the THORP analysis, having attempted to get a 20 per cent cut.

Nor has BNFL obtained the amount of business which it

once expected to get from its UK customers. I am not even sure that the business it appeared to get in 1995, after a couple of decades of uncertainty, is 'secure' in the sense that most reasonable people would understand the term. The THORP contracts apparently agreed by Nuclear Electric and Scottish Nuclear were signed only six weeks before the two companies were told that they would be amalgamated and privatized before the next general election. There must be considerable doubt, therefore, about how firm these THORP agreements will turn out to be, given the fragility of previous 'deals' between BNFL and its UK customers.

If the 1995 agreement sticks, Nuclear Electric's successor company will be contractually committed to having only half of its AGR fuel reprocessed in THORP, some 3,600 tonnes over twenty years. The rest of its AGR fuel will be stored on a 'let's wait and see how well THORP does' basis. Scottish Nuclear will take into the newly privatized generating company a similarly half-hearted commitment to THORP. It is down to have some 1,700 tonnes of AGR fuel reprocessed over twenty years and has talked BNFL into agreeing to have the remaining lifetime arisings of its AGR fuel – an estimated 1,044 tonnes – sent to Sellafield for storage, with no certainty over what will happen to it in the end. This is not at all what was intended when the THORP project was first mooted.

Under the 1995 deal, the Scottish Nuclear fuel will be stored at Sellafield in existing ponds, pending a decision on whether it should be reprocessed or conditioned for final disposal in some other way. BNFL will also pursue discussions with the successors to SN on how dry-store technology can be further developed and exploited – a sop to the Scots, who dropped their plans for building dry stores at Torness and Hunterston. When the Scottish Nuclear deal was announced, Neville Chamberlain described reprocessing and dry storage as 'complimentary [*sic*] spent fuel management techniques'. His predecessor, Con Allday, who always argued vociferously against dry storage, must have winced when he read that comment.

While BNFL maintained that the reprocessing option was still open for the 1,044 tonnes of AGR spent fuel sent to Sellafield for storage by Scottish Nuclear, SN itself appeared to hold out no hope of that ever happening. It stated very plainly when it signed the deal, 'Storage of the 1,044 tonnes will be until the year 2086 or until a repository is available, whichever is the earlier.' THORP will certainly not be working ninety years from now. It seems to me that although Sellafield might not become the world's nuclear dustbin, it is in distinct danger of becoming a trash can for unreprocessed fuel from Scotland, England and Wales.

THORP's commercial position was further eroded at the end of 1994, after the Whitehall appraisal exercise was completed, when two of BNFL's German customers, who have enough storage capacity at their reactor sites for about ten years of spent-fuel arisings, decided to withdraw from commitments they had made to have a total of 545 tonnes of spent fuel reprocessed during THORP's second ten years of operation. The first cancellation, involving fuel from the Krummel power station near Hamburg, amounted to 125 tonnes and the second, from a Bavarian plant operated by RWE and Bayernwerk, covered some 420 tonnes of spent fuel.

The lost German business would have been worth £360 million to BNFL. Although it stood to recover £100 million in compensation, the cancellation of these contracts by the two German utilities came as a considerable blow to the company, reviving concerns that there might be a stampede out of reprocessing by other overseas customers. German utilities still had 790 tonnes of spent fuel committed to post-baseload reprocessing at the beginning of 1995, but there was speculation that all of this business might be cancelled over the following eighteen months. Hopefully this will not happen.

Another possibility which was being canvassed was that

rather than cancelling their contracts the remaining German customers, less well off for reactor site storage, might try to convert them into contracts for interim storage in the THORP complex, with the possibility of reprocessing later if technical improvements could be made to THORP which led to lower prices, following much the same line taken by Scottish Nuclear.

The loss of German business was always something BNFL feared and only the personal efforts of Neville Chamberlain prevented an early flight from reprocessing by the Germans. Now that it has happened, BNFL will be hard pressed to find sufficient business to justify operating THORP for a second ten years, a period in which it expected to make increased profits, having recovered its construction costs during the first ten years of operation. South Korea is one of the countries which BNFL is looking to for replacement business.

In summary, many of the assumptions fed by BNFL into the Whitehall appraisal of THORP have turned out to be wrong, making the whole exercise something of a charade. Nevertheless, my former colleagues at BNFL continue to insist that the changes which have taken place are not sufficient to make the plant uneconomic, even if it operates only for ten years. I hope they are right, not only because I want THORP to be a success but because I am concerned about the financial and environmental implications of the only alternative to reprocessing, long-term storage of spent fuel followed by direct disposal.

In any case, the economic argument has become somewhat arid now that THORP is operating. Although the arithmetic is complicated by the need to take account of the costs of decommissioning THORP and disposing of the subsequent wastes, it does not seem feasible that paying for THORP and for an alternative to it as well can be more economic than paying for THORP and dealing with its residual decommissioning costs at the end of its life. My confidence in that judgement is strengthened by conversations I have had with

John Hayles, a former Finance Director of BNFL, who played a considerable part in negotiating the original contracts.

But my belief that THORP will not cost the country money, although it will not make very much either in relation to the size of the investment, is as much an act of faith as anything else. Only time will tell. A business which once looked a sure-fire winner is beginning to look increasingly vulnerable. I do not think that THORP would have been built if we had known twenty years ago what we know now about energy demand and the availability of resources, but that is perhaps taking unfair advantage of hindsight. The possibility of another THORP being built in the UK is remote in the extreme, even if there is a considerable expansion of nuclear power world-wide, which is itself unlikely in the foreseeable future unless some event confirms the global warming theory, frightening governments into action over fossil-fuel burning.

The Liberal-Democrats have been opposed to THORP and oxide fuel reprocessing from the beginning. The Labour Party's position is one of vaguely supportive neutrality. That is the best Jack Cunningham has managed to achieve – and then only by occasional threats to leave the Shadow Cabinet if the Party turned its back on THORP, most vocally when Neil Kinnock came up with the impractical notion that the reprocessing plant might be turned into a dry store. And the Conservatives, apparently the most supportive of the political parties, have shown by dithering for a year over the start-up of THORP that they are unlikely to want any more hassle.

Chapter Three

Waste Management:

The Building They Forgot

BNFL has spent over £2,000 million on the waste management and effluent treatment plant associated with reprocessing since it took over the Sellafield site from the UKAEA in 1971. It has transferred most of these costs on to its customers, who as a result have become increasingly disenchanted with reprocessing. Big as it is, the expenditure so far is only a drop in the ocean. The company still has to dispose of the growing stockpile of radioactive waste at Sellafield and deal with the contaminated debris which will be created when it knocks down the disused buildings which form part of the site's industrial heritage – and that will cost six or seven times as much again.

Despite strenuous and increasingly successful efforts to get costs down, BNFL expects to spend nearly £15,000 million on decommissioning and waste management projects at Sellafield at current, undiscounted prices. This is out of a total provision of £16,871 million at all of BNFL's sites. Even on a discounted basis, the BNFL group as a whole is building up a provision for £10,657 million of decommissioning and waste management costs – and by far the majority of that relates to Sellafield.

Through a combination of mistakes and bad management on the part of BNFL and the massive over-reaction of the Government and the regulatory authorities to the pressure exerted by environmentalists and critical sections of the media, waste management costs have turned out to be a far bigger burden than anyone anticipated when BNFL was formed. The company has been driven to a near zero environmental discharge policy, forcing it to store more and more waste at Sellafield, thus contaminating an increasing number of plants and buildings. Environmentalists, in particular, have long recognized that closing Sellafield down could lead to the end of nuclear power and that one way to do so would be to price the place out of business.

The executive directors of BNFL who transferred over to the company on its formation in 1971 from the UKAEA knew that there had been a lamentable lack of investment in Sellafield for some years. Housekeeping standards on the site had fallen and morale was low. Sir John Hill, the first Chairman of BNFL, also realized that one day the disused buildings and equipment abandoned by the UKAEA would have to be decommissioned. He had been part of the team which investigated the 1957 fire at Sellafield and knew about the mess which it had left behind. There were also derelict military reprocessing plants and other buildings to be mothballed and eventually demolished.

The initial approach the new board of BNFL took towards the Sellafield ghost plants was sensible and pragmatic. It did nothing. There were two arguments in favour of this. First, it meant that the radioactive materials contained in the plants would have time to decay, making them easier to handle. Secondly, there was nowhere for the materials to go. The same arguments are still being applied today. Then, as now, the approach relies on discarded plants and buildings being kept under surveillance on a proper care and maintenance basis, however. This has not always happened.

While I was with BNFL, board visits were paid to several of the abandoned facilities associated with the piles complex, the first military reprocessing plant and the derelict Head End plant. These visits invariably left me – and some of the other directors – extremely concerned about how buildings and structures containing radioactive materials had been allowed to deteriorate, despite the assurances we were given that they were still in a safe condition.

The visit which worried me most was one to a storage pond containing about fifteen tonnes of fuel recovered from the 1957 fire. A retaining wall of this pond was clearly bulging and I found myself involved in a serious discussion with my technical board colleagues about what would happen if it collapsed. No one was in any doubt that this was a real possibility. The consensus was that if the wall did give way, there would be a release of radioactive water and sludge from the pond which would create serious difficulties on the Sellafield site. It would probably be necessary to evacuate a large part of the site, if not all of it, and all work would have to stop. While a major off-site problem was unlikely, there might be some disruption in the local community.

Shortly after our visit, barriers were installed in the water ducts of the piles complex pond, which was subsequently refurbished. But the pond will not be emptied of all fuel and waste until the year 2004 at the earliest. Decommissioning of the original military reprocessing plant, not used for decades, is programmed to be completed on a similar timescale.

Work began some years ago on removing the brickwork and some structural steelwork at the top of the chimney on Pile No. 2 and more recently on Pile No. 1, the one involved in the 1957 fire. The need to get on with the difficult task of decommissioning the two piles, which have been shut down for nearly forty years, became apparent in the late 1980s, when lumps of masonry broke off the pile chimneys, crashing to the ground. Decommissioning work is expected to be completed by the end of the century.

When BNFL was formed out of the UKAEA, responsibility for the piles complex was shared between the two organizations. The UKAEA retained the ownership of the pile buildings and the old blower houses, while the giant chimneys and the spent fuel storage ponds associated with the complex were handed over to BNFL. It was a bureaucratic nonsense, guaranteed to lead to arguments between the two companies about the pace at which decommissioning should take place, and who should pay for it.

The sheer size of the piles complex makes it impossible to forget, but this has not been the case with all of the buildings on the Sellafield site or all of the obsolete equipment which is waiting to be dismantled there. I was involved in two examples of forgetfulness which led to BNFL being pilloried by ministers, environmentalists and journalists and the company having to spend far more than had been planned on waste management projects, as a way of buying itself out of trouble.

In March 1979, less than three years after excavation work had revealed the B38 silo leak which led to the THORP public inquiry and less than a year after BNFL had been given permission to build THORP, they went digging at Sellafield again. This time they discovered that for at least eight years highly radioactive acid had been leaking into the ground from pipework in a building which was supposed to have been shut down twenty-one years earlier. 'People forgot it was there and they shouldn't have,' Con Allday told the *Financial Times* somewhat ruefully.

This leak was from building B701, one of well over 600 buildings on the sprawling, 480-acre Sellafield site. It contained a series of vessels into which some of the highly active liquid waste separated during reprocessing could be channelled. For five years, from 1953 to 1958, these vessels were tapped and twenty-litre batches of the lethal liquid were drawn off and dispatched to Harwell, in Oxfordshire, 300 miles south. There it was used by the UKAEA for some of the world's first experiments on solidifying highly radioactive wastes for permanent disposal. Thirty years later BNFL came to the conclusion that the UKAEA process was not as good as one developed by the French – and bought the French system.

It was only when the Sellafield management started to investigate the water table beneath the site, prompted by the need to know what was happening to the radioactivity which had leaked from the B38 silo, that they found this new source of ground contamination and traced it back to B701, the forgotten building. This new leak consisted of material which was far more radioactive than that which had 'seeped' out of B38 and the building itself had to be approached with extreme care. It was only by poking video cameras into the radioactive building that the Sellafield scientists found out that throughout the years when B701 was supposed to be empty and idle, highly radioactive liquor was still spurting out.

Plant operating instructions dating back to 1961 – three years after B701 was supposed to have been shut down – stated that a sump vessel, which was there to catch any overflows, should be emptied whenever its level reached a certain height. So somebody had obviously known that there might be a problem after B701 was supposedly closed off. The TV cameras showed that the material in this sump had overflowed on to the stainless-steel-clad floor and risen several feet, dangerously close to the top of the cladding on the walls, without anyone being aware of what was going on.

Nuclear inspectors from the Health and Safety Executive questioned twenty-nine members of the Sellafield staff about the incident, from Roy Pilling, who had taken over from Peter Mummery as the head of the site in 1977, down to the foremen. They established that the ground contamination had occurred when radioactive acids leaked through defects in the stainless-steel cladding of B701. Rather more than 100,000 curies of radioactivity, contained in 10,000 litres of liquid –

the volume of a single-decker bus – had leaked into the ground over a period of at least eight years. Less than one-millionth of a curie of radioactivity can be lethal, if the wrong sort of activity affects the wrong part of the body. The site's discharge authorization limit at that time was 300,000 curies a year. The current limit is 10,800 curies a year.

After the event B701 was cleaned up and physically isolated from other, associated plants containing radioactive materials. The ground in the immediate area is still contaminated but it is at least now known that the contamination is there and the liquid is continuously monitored for possible movement. So far it has not moved, according to BNFL. It is fixed in a layer of soil about three feet thick, at a depth of ten feet or more, and consists of a mixture of radioactive products.

Most of the radioactivity has decayed, but traces of long-lived isotopes such as plutonium remain, locked into the soil below ground level. The surface layer of soil around B701 was not contaminated and this prevented the leak from presenting a hazard to the workforce, some of whom must have walked past the area hundreds of times over the eight years or more that the leak went undiscovered and subsequently. It is still shielding them from harm today. The B701 building is still there too, waiting to be demolished when there is somewhere for the debris to go.

When the Nuclear Installations Inspectorate of the Health and Safety Executive reported on the B701 leak in July 1980, BNFL admitted that it had scored a spectacular own goal. There was no attempt to play down the importance of this event, as there had been at the time of the B38 silo leak. The company acknowledged that over the years there had been several errors of judgement and departures from proper safety standards. BNFL promised to strengthen the organization by which safety was managed at Sellafield. I believe it has done so – but at a very considerable cost, which would almost certainly not have been incurred if proper attention had been paid to safety procedures.

BNFL plans to deal with the fixed contamination beneath both B38 and B701 as part of a programme for waste retrieval and decommissioning agreed with the regulators in line with site licence conditions. Until a waste disposal route is established, however, there seems little point in pressing ahead with this work. The contamination will have to remain where it is, along with the soil contaminated over the years by what Sellafield calls minor spillages. It was often said when I worked for BNFL that if you dug a hole virtually anywhere on the Sellafield site there was every chance that you would find some radioactive contamination.

The B701 leak was discovered just before the Labour Party lost the 1979 general election. It may be just as well for BNFL, Sellafield and the THORP project that it did. In a speech made during the election campaign Tony Benn expressed his concerns about nuclear safety following the Three Mile Island reactor accident in the US and the B701 incident at Sellafield. He revealed that he had asked the Government's chief nuclear inspector to consider whether all or part of the Sellafield site should be shut down.

In his speech Tony Benn argued that the new Government must mount a major inquiry into safety at Sellafield. The incoming Conservative Government either listened to him or had concerns of its own, because as soon as it took office it asked the Nuclear Installations Inspectorate to carry out a comprehensive evaluation of safety at the site. Their safety audit (for which BNFL had to pay) took nearly two years and was very expensive. But carrying out the improvements demanded by the inspectors cost a great deal more. They made fifteen detailed recommendations for improvements, which took BNFL several years to complete. They also said that by the early 1970s Sellafield's safety had deteriorated to an unsatisfactory level, a situation which 'should not have been allowed to develop, nor should it be permitted to occur again'.

Prompted by the B701 incident, and without waiting to

hear what it might be told to do by the Nuclear Installations Inspectorate, BNFL examined all the plants on the Sellafield site, to make sure that old buildings and equipment were safe and there had been no further leaks. No other leaks were found, but there can be no absolute guarantee that none occurred before 1980 or, indeed, subsequently. The ground beneath Sellafield may still hold a few nasty surprises.

Con Allday and the BNFL board were left in no doubt about how seriously the new Conservative Government regarded the B701 incident. Four ministers from the Department of Energy and the Department of the Environment made the long journey up to west Cumbria during the summer of 1980 to express their concern. One of them was Michael Heseltine, then Secretary of State for the Environment, but later responsible directly for Sellafield as President of the Board of Trade. He gave Con Allday a roasting about the state of the site, having been briefed by his officials to make a detour to some of the worst plants during his works tour, rather than accept the carefully chosen itinerary suggested to him by BNFL. Mr Heseltine chose the lunch associated with the visit to give Con a dressing-down in front of his senior Sellafield managers, which was neither popular nor fair, given that Con could hardly answer back.

Certainly there was a strong feeling among the BNFL directors that although conditions at Sellafield were unsatisfactory, this was mainly because other Government-owned organizations, particularly the Ministry of Defence, but also the state-owned electricity utilities, had refused to agree to improvements which they would ultimately have to pay for. The utilities were schizophrenic about Sellafield and there is still an element of that today. On the one hand, they recognized that if Sellafield continued to attract public opprobrium nuclear power might be brought to an end. On the other hand, they could see that soaring reprocessing costs might have exactly the same effect.

Working in poor conditions, in buildings which in some

cases could simply have been improved by a coat of paint, undoubtedly affected the morale of staff at Sellafield. This had already been remarked upon at the THORP inquiry, where it was revealed that between 1950, when reprocessing started, and 1976, there had been 177 incidents at Sellafield which were sufficiently serious to warrant a formal investigation. Most of these incidents were due to comparatively simple errors in design, inaccurate operating instructions and a failure to carry out operating instructions properly.

Some of these factors helped cause one of the most serious incidents to occur at Sellafield, one which led to further considerable expenditure, antagonized many local people who had traditionally been supportive of the site's activities and ruined several careers.

During the early evening of 18 November 1983, I was informed by Roy Pilling, in my capacity as BNFL's Company Secretary and principal troubleshooter, of an unusual release of radioactive material into the Irish Sea. Roy had telephoned me from his office on the top floor of the main administration building at Sellafield to tell me that in the late afternoon sunlight he could see a sheen on the unusually calm sea. A slick of radioactive solvent and crud was floating on the surface and had started to come ashore. This was how I learned of what came to be known as the 1983 Beach Incident, an event which effectively closed local beaches for six months.

Under the company's emergency procedures I had twenty-four hours to decide whether I should report the incident to Government ministers. I confirmed with Roy Pilling that Con Allday had been informed and then agreed that I would get up to Sellafield early the following morning with Con to assess the situation. I then spoke to Con myself and it was clear from our conversation that he had been briefed more fully than I had. Both of us realized that we had a very serious situation on our hands and that ministers would have to be told.

Overnight I began to think about what I had learned earlier

in the week. Two days before Roy Pilling rang me, I had been warned by the Press Office that the *Guardian* had been checking out a story which it had been given by Greenpeace, which was then fairly new to the anti-nuclear scene. According to the environmental group, some of its members had been contaminated on Monday 14 November while diving from a rubber dinghy and taking samples off the end of the Sellafield sea discharge pipeline.

I was sufficiently concerned that I had spoken to John Donoghue, Head of Safety and Medical Services at Sellafield. He had assured me that the Greenpeace people would have received no more contamination than might be expected if they were foolhardy enough to dive off the end of the pipeline and we made a public statement to this effect. John said that he had no reason to believe that there had been an unusually high discharge of radioactive material to the sea, particularly as the reprocessing plant was shut down for annual maintenance. I know from evidence which he later gave to the police that John Donoghue was not hiding anything from me. It was simply that despite his position, he too had not actually been informed of the full situation.

When Con and I arrived at Sellafield's emergency control room on Saturday morning we learned that the incident had its roots in something which had occurred eight days earlier, on 11 November, when the Magnox reprocessing plant was being washed out. As the result of a management error, about 4,500 curies of radioactive liquid, including solvent and particulate matter, or crud, was transferred to one of the sea tanks where low-level waste is held for a final check to be made on its radioactivity content before it is discharged into the Irish Sea.

Although the liquid was more radioactive than usual, discharging all of the contents of the tank to sea would still have been well within the authorization limits then current, and because of this the site management argued that they had no reason to draw the matter to the attention of Con Allday, Peter

Mummery, their previous boss, who was by then Director of Health and Safety and based at Risley, or me. Nevertheless, the site managers were sufficiently concerned that they decided to recover as much of the material which had inadvertently reached the sea tank as possible. The only way to do this was by pumping the material into a medium-active storage plant, B211, through a rarely used emergency return pipeline which was only two-thirds of an inch in diameter. They estimated that this process would take up to seven days and began pumping on the same day.

A day later, largely because a seven-day pumping programme would have led to delays in completing the site maintenance programme, the Sellafield management decided to change their strategy. Believing that most of the liquid at the top of the sea tank consisted of only mildly radioactive liquor of the kind normally discharged into the sea, they stopped the transfer back to B211 and pumped this low-active material out to sea. When their somewhat rudimentary instrumentation indicated a rise in activity in the liquor being pumped out, they stopped the discharge and resumed pumping the higher level waste in the bottom of the tank back to B211 through the emergency return pipeline.

Two days after the start of the incident, normal operation of the sea tanks and the pipelines out to sea was resumed. During the forty-eight hours which had elapsed between the time they recognized that they had a problem and the time they thought it was all over, the Sellafield managers had carried out a whole series of novel operations, including off-site monitoring for above-normal radiation levels. Any one of these activities should have been enough to make them realize that there was at least a risk of the press hearing about the incident.

Likely press interest was and is one of the criteria for reporting an incident to Government ministers, who do not like to be wrong-footed by the media hearing of untoward events before them. An enhanced level of off-site monitoring should also trigger a ministerial report. On both counts the

Sellafield management should have sought my advice. They must have suspected that the press would be interested in what was going on and as several hundred employees knew something of the situation, they must also have realized that there was every likelihood that the press would be tipped off. Sellafield leaks in more senses than one.

The managers had used an emergency return pipe back from the sea tanks to B211. They had sent men out to measure the radiation coming off the sea discharge lines. They had flushed out the sea tanks. They had considered barriering off parts of the site because of high radiation levels. And between Sunday 13 November and the evening of Friday 18 November, when Con Allday and I were told about the incident, they had sent divers out to sea to monitor what Greenpeace was up to and had told local inspectors from the Department of the Environment and the Ministry of Agriculture, Fisheries and Food something of what was going on. Yet the Sellafield management had still not felt it necessary to tell anyone at BNFL's headquarters at Risley.

Con Allday and I were therefore far from pleased as we arrived at Sellafield to assess the situation that Saturday, but we had agreed in the car going up to Cumbria that the inquest could wait. Our first responsibility was to work out with the management what should be done about the solvent slick, which could no longer be seen. After a week of calm water the sea was now a lot rougher and the slick had dispersed, leaving the radioactive solvent washed up on the beach. The Sellafield team clearly felt that they had been the victims of bad luck. I got the distinct impression that there had been similar discharges of solvent and crud in the past, but the strong tides and heavy swell of the Irish Sea could normally be relied upon to carry the material away from the shore and disperse it.

Con and I learned that members of the UKAEA constabulary had already been sent down to the beach near the end of the Sellafield discharge pipeline to warn people to stay away.

There could be no doubt that by issuing this warning to the public the management had established the incident as one which must be reported formally to ministers and that staff and trade union representatives, members of the Sellafield local liaison committee and the press must also be informed.

In discussion with the Sellafield management, I prepared the formal reports and the press statements which were issued by BNFL over that weekend. I have to say that I take no pride in them. While I do not believe that anyone set out to mislead the public or me, these first statements were inaccurate and far too reassuring. This is always a risk when an attempt is made to comment rapidly on a developing situation. The alternatives are to keep quiet, risking accusations of a cover-up, or to have the courage to admit uncertainty, which would probably frighten people even more, but would at least have the merit of being honest.

The first public statement we issued spoke of a small slick of solvent, containing 500 curies of radioactivity, being discharged to sea over the previous weekend, which is what I was told had happened. Subsequently it was estimated by the Government regulators that it was more than likely that nearly all of the 4,500 curies which had reached the sea tank by accident had gone out to sea – a figure which BNFL still disputes – and that it was by no means certain when this happened. Maybe Greenpeace had been right. We also told the public that low levels of contamination had been identified on the beach in the immediate vicinity of the Sellafield site but that it represented no hazard to the public – despite having already told them to keep off the beach. The Government subsequently found it necessary to advise the public not to use a twenty-five-mile stretch of local beaches.

However, the day after issuing these first statements, BNFL announced that all was well. I drafted the all-clear statement in consultation with Sellafield, having been told that radiation measurements taken on the beach were back to normal and that full public access had been restored to the small section of the beach affected. A relatively insignificant amount of contaminated material had been collected and removed for disposal, I was told.

Unfortunately, the situation was still far from normal. Bits of radioactive flotsam kept turning up on the beach, some of them giving off fairly high levels of radiation, certainly much higher than could be allowed on a public beach. After ten days of this, the Department of the Environment decided enough was enough and issued a statement which once more advised the public to avoid 'unnecessary use' of the beaches. It kept this warning on for six months, until the middle of May the following year, extending the area it covered as rubbish continued to be washed up further and further away from the Sellafield site. The Department did not say people could not use the west Cumbrian beaches, but the press interpreted this as a ban and to all intents and purposes it was. I would certainly not have allowed my grandchildren on any of the affected beaches.

Even when the Department of the Environment eventually withdrew its advice, it still felt it necessary to warn people not to remove objects from the beach as there was a small risk of them being contaminated. The main concern was that members of the public, particularly children, might pick up one of the small pieces of radioactive debris being washed ashore and hold it for several hours, burning the skin. Worse still, a child might put such material – bits of plastic, rubber or string – in his or her mouth and swallow it. The advice not to pick up things from the beaches continued throughout that summer, infuriating local shopkeepers and hoteliers and Jack Cunningham, who was annoyed not only about the event but that once more it had taken BNFL so long to announce it.

Peter Walker, then the Secretary of State for Energy, made it clear to Con Allday that he expected to see heads roll following the beach incident, but Con remained loyal to his staff at Sellafield, as he had been at the time of the B38 and B701 incidents previously. Con's own position as Chief

Executive was in jeopardy as a result of his refusal to find a scapegoat and he asked me what I thought he should do. I told him that if he was not prepared to sack somebody over the incident, he had better be seen to be taking some other action, such as a massive management reorganization.

That is what Con did, and to an extent it worked. Roy Pilling, already a board member, was pulled back to Risley, as Peter Mummery had been after the B38 event. Roy, once Peter's deputy at Sellafield, now became his boss, setting up tensions which lasted for some time. Gordon Steele, the general manager of BNFL's fuel-making factory at Springfields, near Preston, was sent up to Cumbria to take over responsibility for Sellafield. There was a realignment of board responsibilities and a mass of management changes affecting most of the BNFL factories. BNFL also announced a new package of site effluent disposal improvements costing tens of millions of pounds. Once more, management mistakes had pushed the company into a fresh round of unplanned heavy expenditure.

I felt desperately sorry for Con Allday. He had been the architect of BNFL's transformation from a Civil Service-oriented organization into something approaching a commercial company, despite interference from the Civil Service and from Government. He had led the company's successful fight to win planning approval for THORP, impressing everyone – even opponents – with his performance as the company's principal witness at the public inquiry. He had led the BNFL board from the front and taken a great deal of personal abuse from Government ministers, the press, even other people in the nuclear industry, as a result.

The irony was that Con had always fought for higher investment levels at Sellafield in an attempt to stave off the sort of incident which had just happened. It was sickening that his career should draw towards its close on such a sour note.

I also felt considerable sympathy for Roy Pilling, who had done a tremendous job at Sellafield, improving housekeeping standards, restoring morale and commissioning new plants while maintaining the reprocessing throughput from old ones. Roy had not even been on the Sellafield site when the first, crucial decisions were taken which led to the Beach Incident. Now he had been sidelined because of it. Many of his colleagues, including me, believed that Roy Pilling was destined to become Chief Executive when Con Allday, who was nearly sixty-three at that time, retired. Now that was clearly not going to happen.

The other person who suffered unfairly was Donald Avery, the Deputy Chief Executive, who decided to carry on with his planned early retirement while all this was happening. Some newspapers assumed from his departure that he must have been responsible for the handling of the Beach Incident and speculated that he had left as a result of it. In fact, Donald had absolutely nothing to do with the management of the incident. It was a rotten way to end a distinguished career.

While all this management reorganization activity created enough interest for talk of dismissals to die down, it did not prevent the company being prosecuted over the 1983 Beach Incident. More than 100 members of the Sellafield staff were interviewed by the Cumbrian police as part of a massive investigation into what had happened. There was talk of individuals being prosecuted and some employees sought an assurance from me, as Company Secretary, that BNFL would stand by them if this happened. I was advised by my Legal Directorate colleagues that I must not provide such a blanket assurance, in case someone had acted maliciously. It was a highly traumatic experience for many employees, as accusations and counter-claims flew around the site about who was responsible for the event. There was a definite rift between the management and the workforce as people looked to save their own skins.

As a result of the Beach Incident, Sellafield's annual maintenance shutdown had to be extended by several weeks so that additional work demanded by the Department of the

Environment and the Nuclear Installations Inspectorate could be carried out. New plant had to be installed, new management control procedures were brought in and thousands of operating instructions were reviewed and, where necessary, rewritten. All this extra work again cost the company millions of pounds and relations with the regulatory authorities became very strained.

Eventually, on 23 July 1985, after a seven-week trial by jury in Carlisle, BNFL was found guilty on three charges relating to the 1983 Beach Incident, pleaded guilty to a fourth and was found not guilty on two others on the judge's direction. Fines totalling £10,000 were imposed on the company, which was also ordered to pay the prosecution's costs up to a maximum of £60,000. That may not sound a lot for a company as big and as rich as BNFL, but the true cost of the incident was, of course, much greater than that, financially and in terms of the public's perception of safety at Sellafield.

Most of the guilty verdicts brought in at the trial related to charges of not keeping adequate records, where the company knew it was vulnerable, but one was concerned with Sellafield not keeping discharges of radioactive materials to the environment 'as low as reasonably achievable' – the so-called ALARA principle. I have always regarded this principle as most unreasonable and virtually unworkable. What is low? What is reasonable? What is achievable? And who decides? It seems to me that specific and quantified discharge limits are infinitely preferable to this vague concept, a catch-all rule brought in by regulators unable to foresee all of the difficulties they expect the operators to be aware of and guard against.

It was because of ALARA, and the company's promise to do even more to reduce levels of radioactive discharges to the Irish Sea as a palliative to public opinion after the Beach Incident, that BNFL now embarked on a capital expenditure programme which in my opinion no other industry would have contemplated. That programme was agreed under pressure and in a hurry and was clearly not properly costed in advance.

Effluent treatment facilities on the so-called Nine Acre Site at Sellafield, which came about directly as a result of the Beach Incident, cost BNFL in excess of £500 million out of the total of £2,000 million the company has spent on waste management and effluent treatment plant since its formation. Included in this is the £166 million spent on a plant called the Enhanced Actinide Removal Plant (EARP) which, according to the independent Radioactive Waste Management Advisory Committee, will reduce discharges by an amount which will theoretically save two lives in 10,000 years.

Effectively, this values a human life at £83 million. This contrasts with the value of a few tens of thousands of pounds placed on a human life by Government when it assesses the cost of carrying out road safety improvements and is clearly a nonsense, although I refused to be led into saying so when I did television interviews at the time. There are no prizes for getting involved in a public debate about the value and sanctity of human life.

As a result of the vast expenditure which has taken place, routine discharges of radioactive materials to the environment, principally into the sea but also into the air, are now less than 1 per cent of the levels which they reached at their peak, around the time I joined BNFL twenty years ago. And high as they were – well over 300,000 curies a year at one stage – even those levels were considered safe by the regulatory authorities at that time. Not all of the expenditure on reducing discharges can be justified in environmental terms. Much of it was a wildly expensive piece of defensive public relations, forced on BNFL by the mistakes of the management and workforce at Sellafield. If the object of the exercise was to save lives, then the money would have been better spent on new hospitals and the equipment for them, on medical research – or on road safety.

The positive side of all this endeavour is that BNFL has

developed techniques and designed plants devoted to the management of radioactive wastes which are the envy of the world, creating a business with considerable commercial potential. In the UK the Health and Safety Executive has already identified the Atomic Weapons Establishment at Aldermaston and the UKAEA's Dounreay site as being in need of improvements of the kind made at Sellafield and this has been accepted by their respective managements.

In the US, Department of Energy politicians and officials have admitted that some of their nuclear sites are in a far worse state than Sellafield. And in the former USSR the problem is even worse, although it is unlikely that much will be done about it, given the lack of financial resources.

Something is being done in the US, where BNFL Inc., formed by BNFL at the instigation of Neville Chamberlain to pitch for waste management business and of which I was a founder board member, now shows enormous promise after a slow start. The company made a real breakthrough in 1995 when it won a £175 million contract to become part of a team carrying out environmental restoration and waste management work at Rocky Flats, a former nuclear weapons site in Colorado, for the US Department of Energy.

Around £200,000 million is expected to be spent on the clean-up of nuclear sites in the US over the next thirty years and even a tiny slice of that business would be worth a lot to BNFL, fully justifying Neville Chamberlain's vision and personal commitment to the BNFL Inc. venture. The company is also trying to become involved in the US programme designed to get rid of plutonium from dismantled nuclear weapons by mixing the plutonium with uranium to form MOX for burning in its civil nuclear power reactors.

While there have undoubtedly been major improvements in waste management at Sellafield, much remains to be done and the final problem, that of waste disposal, still has to be tackled. Ways have to be found of getting rid of the growing volume of radioactive material which is now being stored rather than dispersed into the environment. To develop a radioactive waste repository in the UK will cost at least as much again as BNFL has spent on waste management so far. That task is being undertaken by United Kingdom Nirex Limited, an associate company of BNFL, of which I was also a director. Once again, it is an activity centred on Sellafield, largely because of initiatives which I took in the 1980s.

Chapter Four

Waste Disposal:

The Four Sites Saga

The safety issue which most concerns the nuclear industry and members of the public is the disposal of radioactive waste. One might therefore expect UK Nirex Limited, the company charged with the task of finding and developing an underground burial ground for much of this waste, to have the wholehearted support of its shareholders, the major nuclear companies, and their shareholder, the Government. Unfortunately, this has not been the case in the past and I doubt whether it is today or will be in the future.

Nirex's direct shareholders are BNFL, Nuclear Electric, Scottish Nuclear and AEA Technology. These companies are not only shareholders of Nirex, however, they are also its principal customers, creating obvious tensions over the management of a project estimated to cost well in excess of £2,000 million. The situation is made worse by the fact that all of those involved know that there is a possibility that all or most of the development expenditure will be wasted if Nirex encounters insuperable geological difficulties at the last moment and is forced to abort the project.

There is a further complication in the case of BNFL. Largely at my instigation, Nirex is now concentrating its search for a suitable disposal site underneath Sellafield, with an access point on BNFL-owned land. This has led the majority of BNFL's directors to take the view that BNFL should take over the project from Nirex. An attempt to bring this about was nearly made during 1993, but it was blocked by BNFL's then relatively new Chairman, John Guinness. The Nirex staff are well aware of BNFL's predatory instincts and this has led to divisions within the board and to suspicions and tensions at the working level.

The Government has created equal uncertainty in the minds of the Nirex staff by withdrawing its support from the company at politically expedient moments, severely damaging staff morale. This has invariably been at considerable expense to the nuclear industry too, although this has never been a particularly important consideration for the government when the chips have been down. Despite contrary scientific advice, lack of political resolve has led to the abandonment of a whole series of nuclear waste disposal initiatives over the years and could yet be the undoing of the Sellafield project. As the Nirex underground exploration programme is now well under way there, however, and as the exploration is taking place in a Labour-held constituency rather than one held by the Tories, there is a chance that this time the Government will keep its nerve.

It has taken far too long for the nuclear industry to get to the stage it has now reached on underground waste disposal. When I left the nuclear industry, Nirex was working to a target date of 2006–7 for the operation of the Sellafield underground repository. Because of planning delays, the first waste emplacement is now unlikely to take place until 2012, if then. The disposal of solid radioactive waste, like the dispersal of liquid and gaseous effluents into the environment, should have been given far more attention at the start of nuclear power.

But the problem was deferred for later generations to deal with. The reason for this was that in volume terms waste disposal is not a particularly big issue, although in the absence of a solution it is growing in importance. And volume is not the most important criterion. Keeping millions of curies of radioactivity away from the environment is. The developing problem of solid radioactive waste disposal was first drawn to public attention nearly twenty years ago in the 'Sixth Report of the Royal Commission on Environment Pollution', the Flowers Report. This report, which appeared in 1976, just after I joined BNFL, caused considerable consternation, not least because Sir Brian Flowers, as he was then, was a highly respected member of the UKAEA. There was a feeling within BNFL that Sir Brian had let the side down by putting his name to a report which was critical of the nuclear industry in several important respects.

Nuclear waste is categorized as either high-level waste (HLW), intermediate-level waste (ILW) or low-level waste (LLW). HLW is a concentrated liquid waste produced from the reprocessing of spent nuclear fuel at Sellafield. ILW consists of the irradiated cladding stripped off spent nuclear fuel, reactor components, chemical process residues and filters and resins used to trap radioactive wastes during reprocessing. LLW is mildly radioactive rubbish such as discarded protective clothing, paper towels and worn-out or damaged plant and equipment.

The Flowers Report concentrated on the need to find a way of disposing of high-level waste, which contains over 95 per cent of all the radioactivity present in the waste and is heat generating, making disposal more difficult, and remains so for fifty years or more. But there is not much of it. After more than forty years of reprocessing at Sellafield, the volume of HLW stored there in high-integrity stainless-steel tanks is equivalent to that of four double-decker buses, an analogy which BNFL is fond of using in its advertising. Nevertheless, HLW is lethal and the Flowers Report insisted that storing it as a liquid, with the obvious risk of a leak, was not a long-term solution.

The Royal Commission called for more scientific research on the solidification of HLW and fifteen years later, in 1991 (which hardly reflects the sense of urgency called for in the Flowers Report) Michael Heseltine, then Secretary of State for the Environment, opened the £150 million Windscale Vitrification Plant at Sellafield. In this plant the liquid waste is mixed with molten glass and allowed to cool inside a stainless-steel container, forming a solid block. After early teething problems, this plant is now working well, according to BNFL, although the company's 'medium-term' target of producing 400 containers of solid HLW a year has not yet been reached and it has been necessary for the company to approve the construction of a third production line to provide further vitrification capacity.

The Flowers Report also recommended that there should be a substantial programme of research into the disposal of solidified high-level waste, probably in underground geological formations, and some work was done on this as an immediate response to the report. But not much. In 1977, the UKAEA, acting as agent for the Department of the Environment, was to begin testing the retention charactistics of hard rock, but in the event the HLW generic disposal site investigation programme, as it was called, had reached only the stage of planning approval being sought for test drilling in various parts of the country when the programme was abruptly cancelled by the Government because of public opposition.

Although the UKAEA team was at pains to emphasize that it wanted only to study different geological formations to assess their potential for waste disposal, not to check out specific disposal sites, few local people living in the areas chosen for investigation believed them. Protest meetings were staged all over the country, attracting considerable media interest – and on 16 December 1981 the Government announced a change in policy. It had decided that there was no need for early exploratory drilling for the disposal of HLW after all. All outstanding planning applications were therefore dismissed and others which were pending were withdrawn.

My BNFL colleagues were delighted with the Government's decision, as they had never really accepted the Flowers analysis of the problem. They argued that the best and most practical option, on cost as well as environmental grounds, was for HLW to be stored at Sellafield for at least fifty years, by which time it would have cooled sufficiently for it to be treated as though it was intermediate-level waste, the next category down from HLW, and disposed of in the same way. Later research showed this to have been optimistic: some HLW will take 700 years to reach that stage.

The Government's decision to abandon geological research into the disposal of HLW would be easier to justify if some organization had then been given clear responsibility for working on the scientific, technical and environmental issues surrounding its eventual disposal. But this did not happen. Nirex has responsibility for finding a disposal route for nearly all of the intermediate- and low-level waste stored in the UK, but not for HLW. It is BNFL's job to safeguard the HLW stored at Sellafield, but not to get rid of it. Any research into the disposal of HLW – and little if any was going on when I left the nuclear industry – is the responsibility of the Department of the Environment. To confuse matters further, the main disposal facility for LLW currently in operation is owned and managed by BNFL, not Nirex. One organization should be made responsible for the disposal of all forms of radioactive waste.

It is not yet known where solid and cooled blocks of HLW will go. In 1991 the Radioactive Waste Management Advisory Committee, established in response to one of the recommendations of the Flowers Report, said that there appeared to be no engineering or hydrogeological reasons why HLW (or even spent fuel) could not be disposed of in a deep repository developed adjacent to Nirex's planned ILW/LLW repository and using the same access system. This caused considerable embarrassment to Nirex, which immediately denied that it had any such plans. But the Sellafield area must be a prime candidate for a HLW disposal facility one day. No other part of the country will accept it.

Having stopped looking for a disposal site for HLW in 1981, the Government announced that 'priority' would be given to the disposal of ILW and LLW. It obviously hoped that there would be less public opposition to the disposal of these less-active products. I said at the time that I did not believe this. It seemed obvious to me that people with no real feel for the radiological significance of the different waste categories would be concerned about the disposal of any radioactive waste near where they lived – particularly as the amount of ILW to be buried was equivalent to the volume of eighty double-deckers to use the BNFL analogy, and the LLW to 1,200.

In fact, the Government and the industry took a further step backwards. Since 1949, the industry had dumped a sizeable part of its LLW and ILW into the depths of the Atlantic Ocean – over 2,000 tonnes a year towards the end of the programme. In 1982, prompted by Greenpeace, the National Union of Seamen began a campaign to stop this practice and in 1983 the Government capitulated. It suspended the sea dump and called for a study to be made. Donald Avery, who had overall responsibility for waste management on the BNFL board at that time, was optimistic that this study, led by Professor Fred Holliday, would pave the way for a resumption of sea dumping.

I was much less sanguine. In my experience, politicians are unlikely to resume any practice which the media has become excited about once it has been halted for investigation. There was sufficient ambivalence about the Holliday Report for the

Government to take the soft option and retain its ban on sea dumping. With no particular logic, however, the Government at first insisted that it was keeping open the option of dumping large items such as boilers from decommissioned power stations beneath the sea 'some time in the future' but under pressure from other countries it eventually accepted an indefinite ban on deep ocean disposal of all ILW and LLW, despite protesting that the practice caused no real harm.

When the sea dump was first 'suspended' there seemed to be a chance that a quick solution would still be found to the ILW disposal problem. The management at ICI's Billingham site owned a disused anhydrite mine and offered it for assessment by Nirex as a possible disposal facility for ILW 'in the national interest' – but at a price, of course. They convinced the nuclear industry that they could carry local support for the project, but they failed to do so and abandoned Nirex, which took all of the criticism for trying to impose its will on virgin nuclear territory. In March 1984 the ICI board blocked the Nirex investigation.

Following the Billingham fiasco, Nirex announced that it would try to find somewhere else to bury short-lived ILW – that is, ILW which loses most of its radioactivity within a few decades – shelving the problem of what it would do with longer-lived ILW. Nirex said that it also intended to bury LLW at this new site, because of industry fears that the existing 300-acre site for LLW disposal operated by BNFL at Drigg, a few miles along the coast from Sellafield, would run out of space by the end of the century. Drigg is used as a dump for LLW which BNFL receives not only from the nuclear industry but also from hospitals, universities, research institutions and other industries as well. There are over 7,000 registered users of radioactive substances in the UK.

BNFL overstated the space problem at Drigg because it did not believe that Nirex was getting anywhere and wanted to stretch out Drigg's life to ensure that reprocessing at Sellafield was protected. But the main reason for the longer life now ascribed to Drigg is BNFL's pricing policy, which was heavily criticized by the Energy Select Committee in 1989. Between 1986 and 1989 BNFL imposed an eightfold price increase at Drigg, and although the company pointed out that the annual cost to the UK generating boards of using the site was still only £330,000 this price hike undoubtedly soured relationships. But it did make those organizations which send LLW to Drigg for disposal, including BNFL's own factories, much more careful about segregating the waste before it is dispatched, reducing overall volumes. It is now thought that Drigg will not be filled until about the year 2030 or beyond.

BNFL justified the Drigg price rises on major improvements which it had made and on the introduction of better disposal methods – changes it had been forced to make in response to criticism from another Commons Select Committee, the Environment Committee. After a visit to Drigg the committee, led by Sir Hugh Rossi, had produced a highly critical report, drawing attention to disposal methods which appeared to the committee's members to be no better than those used at reasonably well-managed local authority rubbish tips.

The committee called for the adoption of 'Rolls-Royce' solutions at Drigg, to reassure the public that radioactive material was being handled carefully. As an exercise in public reassurance, improvements were probably necessary, although they did little to improve radiation protection. As a direct result of the Rossi Report, which received a great deal of media attention, BNFL spent more than £20 million on sprucing up Drigg, carrying out improvements to that part of the site which already contained LLW and adopting new methods for future disposal. The company put plastic sheets over the trenches into which nuclear waste had been tipped from the back of lorries, in order to stop surface water getting in and leaching out radioactivity. It also improved the trench system to provide a means of intercepting and monitoring any leached water before it left the site by pipeline, rather than by way of a local brook.

BNFL also agreed that all future trenches would be concrete-lined, that the waste going into these trenches would be compacted and containerized, rather than just dumped in black plastic bags, and that when the trenches were full they would also be capped with plastic sheets. In presentational terms this was the most important change of all and Sir Hugh Rossi made a point of congratulating BNFL on the improvements when he made a visit to Drigg some years after his early report had been issued.

As a result of BNFL's dire warnings about the limited prospects at Drigg, Nirex started to investigate a site owned by the CEGB at Elstow in Bedfordshire as a possible site for the shallow burial of LLW and short-lived ILW. Later, three further locations were added to the Nirex investigation programme: Bradwell in Essex, Fulbeck in Lincolnshire and Killingholme in Humberside. This marked the beginning of what came to be known within the nuclear industry as 'The Four Sites Saga'.

The management of Nirex, all seconded to the company by its shareholders, felt that at last they had a real job to do. Nirex was initially constituted as the Nuclear Industry Radioactive Waste Executive, but in 1985 it was incorporated as a limited company, UK Nirex Limited. This was done to give its contractors some comfort about its legal status and financial standing, and also provided some reassurance to Nirex employees that the shareholders meant the company to have a future. However, it seemed to me that Nirex was in danger of antagonizing an ever-widening group of people who had no nuclear interests in their neighbourhoods and who stood to gain little economic benefit from nuclear waste disposal.

I began to express the view within BNFL that a solution to the waste management problem – whether it was the disposal of high-, intermediate- or low-level waste – would only be found in or near Sellafield or close to the UKAEA establishment at Dounreay, on the remote north-western coast of Scotland. The communities in these two areas are heavily dependent on the nuclear industry and more familiar with its dangers. They might therefore be expected to accept what other regions would regard as an environmental blight.

Although it was known that I was out of sympathy with the Nirex investigation programme at the four potential sites, or perhaps because I was critical of what was going on, I was nominated by BNFL to the board of Nirex, which I joined in May 1986. As a director of Nirex I now had a legal responsibility to act in its interests. As a director of BNFL I had the same duty towards that company – and it paid my salary. There was an obvious clash of interests, but as I was not the only director with divided loyalties, this was something I accepted. I did nothing to support the four sites' investigation programme, which I regarded not only as a waste of time and money but actually as damaging to the nuclear industry's longer-term prospects of developing a disposal route, but I did nothing to hamper it either.

Although I was convinced that Nirex would not succeed in establishing a waste repository at any of the four sites, I had to admire the effort it put into its attempt to do so, despite the public furore. Tom McInerney, Nirex's Managing Director, who knew that BNFL was not fully behind his efforts, led a team which worked day and night to convince people living near the potential sites that these sites were only being investigated as part of a much wider scientific appraisal programme. Once more, however, despite an extensive programme of lectures and debates and the preparation and distribution of a great deal of explanatory literature, no one believed them. In the end, Nirex used the law to gain access to the four sites and Tom even reported that he believed the company was gaining the grudging acceptance of at least one of the four affected communities. I regarded that as wishful thinking.

It seemed to me that there were two main reasons why

Nirex experienced so much difficulty in opening up the four potential disposal sites. By abandoning the sea dump, ditching Billingham and cancelling the earlier generic geological test programme, the Government had demonstrated that local communities and anti-nuclear groups could oppose Nirex successfully. In addition, because of the pressure it felt under to do something, to open another door as soon as one was slammed in its face, Nirex did not spend enough time smoothing the way before Tom McInerney and his intrepid team marched into a new area.

I was determined that this should not happen at Sellafield. I became increasingly convinced that it represented the nuclear industry's last chance of solving its waste disposal problems. With the agreement of Christopher Harding, who had succeeded Con Allday as Chairman of BNFL, and Neville Chamberlain, who had taken over Con's other role as Chief Executive, I began to hold informal discussions with the principal political players in Cumbria – Jack Cunningham, the Copeland MP, Billy Minto, leader of the controlling Labour group on Cumbria County Council, and Jimmy Johnston, leader of the controlling Labour group on Copeland Borough Council. I was also careful to involve the leading Conservatives in Cumbria, Rex Gingell and Rex Toft of the County Council and Tom Broughton of Copeland Borough Council.

At a series of meetings I began to sow the seeds. I pointed out that well over half of the waste destined for a repository was being stored on the surface at Sellafield. Even if the nuclear power programme was abandoned, this waste would still be there and would still have to be dealt with. I also argued that unless a repository was developed, there must be a threat to the future of reprocessing at Sellafield, the mainstay of the west Cumbrian economy, and to the construction and subsequent operation of THORP, which was only just getting under way.

The politicians I met took these arguments well and began to discuss with me what Cumbria might get out of any repository development by way of planning gain and employment, an obvious sign that there was a chance of them accepting the project and that they might even be persuaded to give it their overt support. I reported back to Christopher Harding and to Neville Chamberlain, who, like Christopher, was still relatively new to the labyrinthine politics of Cumbria. They then started to involve themselves in the discussions which I had begun.

We had still not briefed Nirex or any of the other shareholders in that company on what we were doing. Indeed, there was no intention at that time of getting Nirex involved in any way. This was a BNFL project, in partnership with the local authorities. There was even talk of a joint company being set up, in which Cumbria County Council and Copeland Council would have a minority shareholding, as a way in which they could exert direct influence on how the project was taken forward and as a mechanism for them obtaining what was euphemistically called planning gain by way of dividends.

Meanwhile, Nirex was running into difficulties with its investigation programme at Elstow, Bradwell, Fulbeck and Killingholme. In June 1986, while I was still holding private discussions about a possible Sellafield waste repository, the Government announced that because of the perceptions of local communities (not for any scientific reason) any near-surface repository built in the UK would be restricted to the disposal of low-level waste only. All intermediate-level waste, short- and long-lived, was to be stored until a deep repository became available. Once more the Government retreated in the face of local hostility.

But the Government's partial retreat was not enough to placate people living near the four sites. They could smell blood and continued to press for Nirex to pack up its equipment and go home to Harwell. Ironically, the four sites were all in constituencies held by Conservative MPs, including John Wakeham, who was then the Government Chief Whip. In the run-up to the 1987 general election the activities of Nirex became a major issue in all four constituencies and Nicholas Ridley, then the Secretary of State for the Environment, came under considerable pressure to calm things down.

On Friday 1 May 1987, a bare six weeks before the election, I arrived at Nirex's headquarters on the AEA Technology site at Harwell for a routine board meeting. Tom McInerney informed the assembled directors that he would be running the meeting until John Baker, the Chairman, was free to take over. John, who was also Chief Executive of the state-owned CEGB at the time, was on the telephone to Nicholas Ridley, we were told, and Tom was unable, or unwilling, to tell us what they were talking about. It was all very mysterious.

Around midday John Baker arrived in the boardroom and we were handed a copy of a letter which he had agreed to send to Nicholas Ridley. This said that as a result of comprehensive ground investigations at the four sites, together with work carried out on repository design and radiological and non-nuclear environmental assessment, Nirex had come to the conclusion that the economic advantages of separate near-surface LLW disposal were not as great as had been considered earlier. Although near-surface disposal of LLW would be safe (which was just as well, as this had been the practice at Drigg for decades), the development of a new near-surface repository for LLW showed 'no significant cost advantage' when compared with the marginal cost of disposing of LLW along with ILW in a deep repository, even allowing for the cost of any short-term storage of LLW which might be needed before the repository was developed.

The John Baker letter which we were asked to support as Nirex board members advised the Secretary of State that we had come to the conclusion that it would be preferable to develop a multi-purpose deep site for LLW and ILW. The Nirex board was given less than an hour to discuss the implications of what John Baker had agreed with Nicholas Ridley, which was a blatant device to get the nuclear waste issue off the general election agenda. The reasons given for this new retreat were not very convincing. Even on a marginal cost basis, the disposal of LLW in a deep repository was still nearly twice as expensive as disposing of it near the surface. Nevertheless, we all went along with what John Baker had agreed. It is no excuse, but I think we were all too stunned to debate the issue. As far as I am aware, none of the Nirex directors who attended that fateful board meeting, apart from John Baker and possibly Tom McInerney, knew what was going on in advance. Certainly it came as a complete surprise to Bill Wilkinson, my BNFL colleague on the Nirex board, and to me.

Not surprisingly, Nicholas Ridley accepted John Baker's advice with alacrity and obvious pleasure. He announced in the House of Commons that Nirex would cease investigations of sites for a near-surface repository for LLW and concentrate on the development and construction of a deep multi-purpose facility for the disposal of both ILW and LLW. It was the final chapter of the Four Sites Saga.

At the following week's BNFL directors meeting, I reported what had happened and told Neville Chamberlain that I had spent the weekend considering whether I should resign from the Nirex board, because of my discomfort over the way the decision to abandon the four sites had been taken. Neville asked me what I had decided and I told him that I would stay on. My reasons were mixed. As I had never believed that Nirex had the slightest chance of developing any of the four sites, it seemed illogical to resign because it had stopped investigating them. I also felt that I had something to contribute towards bringing about the successful development of a disposal site at Sellafield. Finally, it has to be said, I ducked out of resigning because I knew that if I did so I could find myself at the centre of a general election row and might lose my job. I am still not sure that I took the right decision.

As it was, Labour attacked Nirex for meekly changing its policy in order to help the Government retain the four Tory constituencies. Nirex's name was mud in Cumbria and although BNFL was a major shareholder, I contrived to distance BNFL from the Nirex decision. The Labour-controlled Cumbria County Council and Copeland Borough Council took years to push the folk memory of what they believed Nirex had done to help the Conservative Party win a general election into the background. They still preferred to regard the Sellafield repository as primarily a BNFL project when I left the nuclear industry, as it so very nearly was.

With the abandonment of the four sites Nirex was left without a programme again and it was only then that BNFL began to talk to the rest of the nuclear industry about the secret discussions I had been having in Cumbria. The hiatus at Nirex provided BNFL with an opportunity to press for Nirex to be wound up and I know that the possibility was discussed by the industry chairmen. But the other Nirex shareholders – all customers of BNFL for reprocessing and therefore capable of exerting considerable influence on the company – made it clear that they were not prepared to see BNFL take over sole responsibility for waste disposal. After the experience of the eightfold price rise at Drigg, they did not trust BNFL to exercise sufficient restraint. The future relationship between Nirex and BNFL with respect to BNFL's plans to investigate the potential of Sellafield as a waste repository site had still not been settled when I announced the project in September 1987. The differences were simply papered over.

This uncertainty probably explains why I was allowed to announce the Sellafield scheme, which was the most important development in the waste disposal area for many years, rather than Christopher Harding or Neville Chamberlain. The press conference which I chaired at Sellafield was carefully managed. Sitting on the platform with me were Jack Cunningham and Jimmy Johnston, the leader of the local council.

The scheme announced was the one favoured by the local authorities and BNFL, involving the construction of a purpose-built repository under the seabed off Sellafield. Access was to be from the Sellafield site and it was envisaged that the likely form of development would be a fully engineered depository – a word the local authorities preferred to respository – in which wastes would be placed in a monitorable and retrievable form. Although this was the scheme we all wanted, we did not know how the concept would be received. I was therefore careful to explain that it was only one of a number of options which BNFL, Copeland Borough Council, Cumbria County Council and local community groups were discussing.

To cover the unresolved position of Nirex, and by agreement, I said that Nirex was backing BNFL's geological investigations on the Sellafield site. It was some time later, and much to the annoyance of Jack Cunningham and the local authorities, that the BNFL board agreed that the company would manage the Sellafield site investigation only as agent for Nirex and not be sole owner of the development. It also agreed to operate any facility which was built on behalf of Nirex and not in its own right. With the Four Sites Saga still fresh in the memory and with the Conservative Party winning the 1987 general election, it would have been impossible to persuade Jack Cunningham or the Cumbrian local authorities to support a project managed and directed by Nirex from the outset and I had to work hard to convince them that Nirex had a role at all.

Jack Cunningham was then Shadow Environment Secretary and showed a lot of courage in openly supporting the Sellafield repository development. He knew this would antagonise environmentalists, whose support the Labour Party had been trying to attract, and some of his constituents as well. Although they had previously demanded that the waste disposal issue be resolved, the anti-nuclear groups were now arguing for the long-term surface storage of wastes and spent fuel instead. Dr Cunningham called for an early start to be made to the geological study at Sellafield. Acknowledging that there might be some hostility to the project locally, he said that the reality was that much of the country's intermediate-level waste was already at Sellafield, held in surface stores. It did not make sense to look for sites elsewhere and to transport very large amounts of nuclear waste around the country.

Jimmy Johnston was equally forthright. He said that BNFL's proposal that ILW waste would be disposed of in a retrievable form, with a long-term commitment to monitoring, could well satisfy local concern regarding waste management practices and environmental impact. At the very least, BNFL's approach towards solving the waste disposal problem provided a basis for serious discussion. It will not be easy for Nirex to keep the waste in a retrievable form but it is important in terms of public acceptability that local people have that assurance, at least until they are satisfied that the waste can be safely abandoned.

With BNFL now in the driving seat at Sellafield, Nirex still clung on to its wider national role and to the increasingly slim possibility that it would eventually be allowed to explore any region of the country which it considered to have geology suitable for its purpose. At this time, nearly a third of the British landmass was assessed by Nirex as potentially having the right geology for a repository and the company talked of no fewer than 500 sites showing some promise. To me that represented 500 communities which had probably not bothered very much about nuclear power previously but which could be expected to become stridently anti-nuclear if any moves were made in their direction. It is as well the 500 sites were never named.

Over the next two years Nirex began to whittle the number of possible sites down, partly by commissioning British Geological Survey to carry out a desk-top review of the geological information already at hand and partly through a massive consultation exercise involving local authorities and any other organizations or individuals claiming to have an interest. The consultation process began in November 1987, two months after I announced what BNFL intended to do at Sellafield, with the publication of a discussion document, 'The Way Forward', which proposed three concepts: a deep repository under land; a repository under the sea bed but reached from the coast; and a repository under the sea bed with access from an offshore rig or artificial island.

The design concept for the repository is based on the principle of multi-barrier containment. This provides for the form of the waste and the way it is packaged, together with engineered barriers in the repository itself, to build up into a total system capable of preventing the movement of radioactivity for very long periods. The ultimate barrier is still the host rock, however, and this must be stable, with no major faults or fractures and with a record of very low seismic activity. It is also important that the rock has a suitable hydrogeological environment – long, slow and predictable groundwater flow paths, preferably towards the sea.

Not unexpectedly, the 'Way Forward' consultation exercise, particularly discussions with those local authorities prepared to speak to Nirex, made it clear that acceptable geology and a favourable water environment would not be allowed to become the sole criterion for siting a repository in a particular area. Most of the local authorities raised the issue which I had long believed to be central to the opposition encountered by Nirex over the years. The main reason people did not want to play host to a repository was that they were afraid of the effect such a development would have on the local economy, especially in areas dependent on tourism, agriculture and fishing, and because they did not want the social stigma associated with the public's perception of radioactive waste disposal.

Fifty thousand copies of the 'Way Forward' discussion document were issued and an analysis of the responses to it carried out by the University of East Anglia provided useful information. The university concluded that there was reasonable support for the deep disposal of radioactive wastes and that local authorities with existing nuclear installations in their areas and the various scientific and advisory bodies who responded did not, on the whole, support the concept of prolonged surface storage. Most importantly, there was little support for disposal under the sea bed.

So much for the idea of burying the waste under the seabed off the Sellafield coast, which was bitterly opposed by the Irish and Isle of Man governments and less popular locally than I had expected. Eventually Jack Cunningham and the other political leaders in Cumbria agreed that a deep repository should be developed on land rather than under the sea – and it is just as well that they did. The early results from the test drilling programme at Sellafield showed that suitable rock was unlikely to be found at manageable depths under the sea. The most promising rock formations were to be found inland, as close as possible to the Lake District National Park, which begins less than a mile over the main A595 road from the edge of the Sellafield site. Indeed there would be more certainty about the outcome of the Nirex programme at Sellafield if it was allowed to tunnel out under the fringe of the National Park itself, instead of stopping about a quarter of a mile from it.

By 1989 Nirex had reduced its list of 500 potential sites to just twelve – including Sellafield and Dounreay. Following consultation with the Government, Dounreay and Sellafield were then selected for initial drilling and it was announced that the suitability of these two sites would be tested before deciding whether it was necessary to evaluate any others. The two sites were chosen quite explicitly because there was some familiarity with the nuclear industry and some support for it.

Nirex and the Radioactive Waste Management Advisory Committee acknowledged that there were other sites which potentially offered better geological conditions and which might therefore be expected to turn out to be more robust in radiological terms. But they both finally recognized that there was no particular virtue in going for a site which would substantially outperform the extremely tight risk targets set for a deep disposal site by the Government, which have the catch-all ALARA principle attached to them as well. Because these targets have to be met for all time and because of the nature of the geology, the repository is likely to be developed at a depth of around 650 metres. This is expected to ensure that any radioactive material washed out of the repository takes a very long time to get to the surface or, preferably, into the sea, and that no one stumbles on the repository inadvertently as part of any future excavation.

The main safety target set by the Government is that the risk of any member of the public contracting cancer as a result of the operation of the repository should not be more than one in a million in any one year. A one in a million risk is the same as that involved in smoking one and a half cigarettes in a lifetime, travelling fifty miles by car or 250 miles by air, climbing for ninety seconds, canoeing for six minutes, engaging in ordinary factory work for between one and two weeks or simply being a male aged sixty for twenty minutes.

The radiation dose represented by that one in a million risk is equivalent to the radiation dose someone would get by flying to Spain ten times, about a third of the dose everyone gets from naturally occurring radioactive materials in their bodies, a twentieth of natural background radiation from the earth's rocks, the sun and outer space, and a two-hundredth of the dose which people living in houses built from granite in several parts of the country get from their surroundings. There is no particular logic in the Government setting tougher radiation limits for the Nirex repository than the levels which occur naturally in the environment, but it has done so. And Nirex has gone even further by adopting a target for its radiation protection studies which is twice as restrictive as that set by the Government, in response to advice from the National Radiological Protection Board that it should treat risks as covering serious hereditary disorders as well as fatal cancers.

Another Government target is that future movement of radioactivity from an underground disposal facility should not lead to a significant increase in the radioactivity which occurs naturally in the general locality of the facility. Given that natural radiation levels vary enormously in different parts of the country, that the level around Sellafield is about the national average and well below some other areas, and that the word significant is not even quantified, that seems to me to be absurd.

It is equally nonsensical that Nirex will have to try to prove at any future public inquiry that it has taken steps to safeguard mankind 'for all time'. This is interpreted by Nirex as meaning for at least a million years, by which time the inventory of radioactive waste contained in the repository will have decayed to truly trivial levels. This period will encompass several Ice Ages, when the sea level is expected to fall by up to 140 metres, exposing any radioactive material which might have leached out of the repository. We discussed that possibility at the Nirex board too, and I expressed the opinion that if man could survive a succession of Ice Ages he might also be expected to cope with the small increment in radiation which he might face from any leached repository materials. I also pointed out that a rather more serious risk was likely to be posed by the many tonnes of radioactive materials already discharged into the Irish Sea from Sellafield as a result of reprocessing.

Having settled on Sellafield and Dounreay as the favoured candidates for a repository, Nirex carried out some exploratory borehole drilling and other geological investigations at both sites. It came to the conclusion that the deep geology at either site could be suitable for the safe disposal of intermediate- and low-level waste and that there was little to choose between the two sites in terms of any non-nuclear environmental impact. Crucially, however, as about 60 per cent of the waste destined for the repository arises at Sellafield, the choice of that site would substantially reduce transport requirements, producing a saving to the nuclear industry of around £1,000 million over the fifty years in which the repository is expected to operate.

In July 1991, four years after I had announced BNFL's interest in establishing a Sellafield repository and getting on for six years since I had started to lobby for support in Cumbria, Nirex announced that it would concentrate its further investigations on Sellafield. It also promised to take into account local concerns about its plans for extensive building in the area between the Sellafield site and the village of Gosforth, where most opposition to the repository was being voiced. Local residents took particular exception to the original Nirex concept of developing the underground repository as a coal mine might be developed, with winding gear, or head works, standing high above the access shafts to the repository and dominating the local skyline.

By the end of the year Nirex announced its new design concept, based on a drift tunnel spiralling underground from an entry point on the Sellafield site, with waste being delivered to the repository along a railway. This avoided the need to hoist heavy and bulky loads down a shaft and the expense of the machinery required to do that in safety. It also reduced the number of surface facilities – including head works – which had to be located alongside the existing BNFL factories at Sellafield. The interesting thing is that the drift mine approach was considered only because of local pressure, and yet it was substantially cheaper than the scheme we had been considering until then. It served to show that the cost comparison carried out before the four sites were abandoned was based on very little in the way of firm financial or engineering information.

I helped Michael Folger, who succeeded Tom McInerney as Managing Director of Nirex in June 1991, to launch the new design concept and it certainly played its part in dampening down local opposition. I also made a point of being with him at local events, to indicate that Nirex and BNFL were now marching in step, although that was not strictly the case. By then I had become a little tired of the regular discussions which still went on within BNFL about whether we should make a play to take over the Sellafield project. I told Michael

Folger that as far as I was concerned the important objective was to get a repository accepted and built, not to change its ownership. It seemed to me that Nirex was finally getting itself into shape to carry out the task of developing the repository and that it should be allowed to press on.

Two new appointments made at this time were crucial in my view, that of Sir Richard Morris as Chairman of Nirex and his appointment of Michael Folger as Managing Director. Although I had known Dick Morris as a director of BNFL, he had been out of the nuclear industry for some years and was free of the baggage of working for one of the shareholder companies. Similarly, Michael Folger was brought in from outside, after a career in merchant banking and the Treasury, and owed no particular shareholder his allegiance either. The other external recruitments which have taken place, together with the decision to cut off the escape route for seconded staff back to their previous employers, has given Nirex much more focus.

The step-by-step approach which Nirex has now adopted, keeping the commitment of shareholders' funds in reasonable step with growth in geological understanding, seems to me to be the right one. The characterization of deep geology is not a risk-free business, but the process will undoubtedly be helped by the rock characterization facility (RCF) which Nirex plans to build for that purpose at a cost estimated in 1993 at about £125 million, which now looks decidedly optimistic.

Nirex had hoped that it would be granted planning permission to develop the RCF without a public inquiry and to reach the appropriate depth by about mid-1996, to be followed by lateral exploration. Unfortunately, its hopes were dashed and the public inquiry called by the Government, which began in September 1995, is likely to add over a year to the repository programme – and to add substantially to overall project costs. A decision is likely towards the end of 1996, and if Nirex receives permission to develop the RCF and if it then decides some years hence, on the strength of the research information obtained from the RCF, that it should go ahead with the repository proper, it will still have to apply for planning permission to do that. There will then most certainly be a further public inquiry – and further expensive delay.

Despite the setbacks, I remain convinced Nirex has a real chance of developing a deep underground repository at Sellafield, an essential prerequisite for a successful nuclear power industry privatization. The design assumption of the repository is that it will take 300,000 cubic metres of intermediate-level waste. Because BNFL finally came clean about the potential of Drigg as a dumping ground for low-level waste, it is now anticipated that the repository will need to take only a nominal 100,000 cubic metres of LLW, far less than was once expected.

To put some perspective on this in volume terms, and as a change from BNFL's double-decker bus analogy, there are already 90,000 cubic metres of ILW held in surface stores in the UK and this, according to Nirex, would cover a football pitch to a height of 40 feet. Deep beneath Sellafield it is the intention to have the equivalent of five such football pitches.

If the geology being investigated underneath Sellafield turns out to be unsatisfactory, then the most sensible thing to do would be to look close by for rock and water flow formations which promise to be more suitable. The objective should still be to access a repository from the Sellafield site. The most suitable local geology for the purpose is known to be beneath the fells to the east of Gosforth, under land owned by the National Trust.

At the risk of being branded an environmental philistine, I believe that if the present repository project founders for geological reasons, the possibility of heading off further inland should be examined seriously. Although it would be important to ensure that there was minimal visual intrusion on the fells, I can see nothing wrong in principle with having the repository deep below the Lake District National Park.

If it is judged to be safe to construct a repository below the heavily populated Sellafield site and closer to the sea, towards which any leached-out radioactive waste will migrate eventually, it should be even safer to build one further away from the coast under land largely inhabited by sheep. No doubt there would even be those who would get some sort of vicarious pleasure out of being able to say that they had walked or driven over the lethal storehouse below the remote west Cumbrian fells.

Chapter Five

Health and Safety:

It's in the Jeans

Politicians, environmentalists, members of the medical profession, a few lawyers and sections of the media have combined over the years to give the impression that there is something uniquely dangerous about working with radiation and that Sellafield's health and safety record is a poor one. I do not accept that either statement is true. Although mistakes have been made and there can never be room for complacency about handling potentially lethal substances, Sellafield's record stands comparison with that of other companies in the chemical and engineering industries. But this is not what the public has been led to believe. The dangers of radiation have been consistently overstated by those determined to get Sellafield shut down and their views have received an inordinate amount of publicity. Public opinion has been further affected by the insensitive way in which purely statistical studies of cancer incidence among the Sellafield workforce, their children and members of the local community have been released and publicized – and that is much less easy to understand or to forgive.

The most exposed member of the public receives only 2 per cent or so of the radiation dose which some Sellafield workers get each year as a result of the site's operations and for most people the gap is far wider. It follows, therefore, that if the health of the workforce is properly safeguarded, then the public's safety will also be ensured, unless there is a disaster such as that at Chernobyl or some smaller event which spreads a significant amount of radioactivity out into the general environment.

Because of BNFL's heavy expenditure on safety equipment and the management of safety and the interest shown by the regulatory agencies, particularly in recent years, the site's employees now have the necessary assurance that they are well protected as far as routine operations at Sellafield are concerned. This has not always been the case, however, and certainly not in the early years of nuclear power or during the course of several on-site incidents which took place when I worked for the company.

The main health effects of radiation fall into two distinct categories: the short-term effects of very heavy doses, which appear soon afterwards, producing radiation sickness within days; and the long-term effects, produced by smaller doses, which can lead to various kinds of cancer, particularly leukaemia, and to genetic effects which may appear many years later. Heavy doses accumulated gradually over long periods of time do not produce acute radiation sickness and their effects are of the long-term kind.

The unit used for measuring radioactivity changed in the 1980s. For consistency I have used the old unit, the curie, rather than the new one, the becquerel. Similarly, I have used the old unit for measuring radiation exposure, the rem (or, where small doses are involved, the millirem, which is a thousandth of a rem) rather than the new one, the sievert. Either the old or new units would serve my purpose, which is to indicate as simply as possible the levels of radioactivity and radiation effect which should give cause for concern.

Knowledge of high radiation doses and acute radiation sickness has come almost entirely from the victims of nuclear weapons, people exposed to massive amounts of radiation, large enough to damage cell membranes and produce extensive internal bleeding, severe anaemia and seriously damaged resistance to infection. The effects of high doses are all too self-evident.

Identifying the effects of low-level radiation is much more difficult, however, calling for judgements to be made on the basis of theory rather than observed fact. Until 1950 it was believed that there was a 'threshold dose' of radiation exposure, below which no harmful effects would occur. Then the industry and its regulators decided to accept the safety first concept that any additional amount of radiation, however small, will do some harm and that there is no such thing as a safe radiation dose. That is an extremely prudent assumption, which carries with it important considerations for the way in which society at large is ordered, as man lives within a naturally radioactive environment, not just how safety in the nuclear industry should be managed. Some of the issues which it raises have only just started to be addressed.

As with many other industries, understanding of the potential health hazards of radioactivity put into the environment by the nuclear industry has increased with time and is still being refined. Nevertheless, when the industry began there was a reasonable amount of information available about the effects of man-made and natural radiation. Radium and X-rays had been in use for fifty years and there were clinical records of the impact which their indiscriminate use had on the health of radiologists and their patients. In addition, the medical use of radiation had led to the deaths of some of those subjected to it. In the UK about 15,000 people had been dosed with nearly 400 rems of X-rays each for the treatment of arthritis of the spine before the dangers of this practice were recognized. They suffered 100 more cancer deaths than would be expected in a population of that size. It is a dreadful irony that radiation, used in the treatment of cancer, can also cause it.

There was also the experience of women employed on painting the faces of watches and other objects with luminous paint in the US in the early 1920s. A significant number of these women developed bone cancers many years later. This was caused by them licking their paintbrushes to make them pointed and swallowing minute quantities of the radium 226 contained in the paint. Radium is a radioactive substance occurring naturally which, once swallowed, concentrates in the bones. The radioactivity of the radium, the source of the luminosity, ate away the mouths, teeth and jawbones of these women. Eventually it eroded the whole skeleton. The victims of this new industrial disease called themselves 'the society of the living dead' and most died before they were thirty. The last survivor, who had worked as a radium girl when she was eighteen, died in 1954, aged forty-eight.

At the start of civil nuclear power in Britain information was also coming out of Japan, where whole populations had been exposed to intense radiation when the atomic bombs were dropped on Hiroshima and Nagasaki. People there had died in horrendous ways. Some, receiving radiation doses of more than 1,000 rems, went quickly, within three days of their exposure to radiation, as a result of extensive internal bleeding and damage to the blood supply to the brain. Others, with slightly lower doses, lasted up to ten days, dying as a result of damage to the intestine. People with doses of around 700 rems died a lingering death over two months or so, their blood-making systems damaged beyond repair.

But there were survivors too, some of whom are still alive and are still given regular medical checks, acting in effect as human guinea pigs for those researching the impact of radiation. Doses below 200 rems produced no immediate effects, although the victims have suffered long-term ill-health, particularly due to anaemia. Below 100 rems the main problem appears to have been an increased risk of cancer. One of the difficulties with the Japanese information, which is still being accumulated, is that even in the case of the survivors it is largely based on relatively high levels of radiation. Hopefully Sellafield will always be concerned with low-level radiation effects only.

When Sellafield started up, all of this knowledge had to be translated quickly into radiation protection standards covering the operation of industrial plants which had to handle enormous quantities of many different kinds of radioactivity, some previously unknown and created only by the nuclear fission process. Regulations also had to be drawn up to govern how much radioactive material could be discharged off-site and dispersed into the environment.

The fission products produced by the burning of uranium in nuclear reactors – and subsequently separated out by reprocessing – consist of thirty-five different chemical elements, all of which behave differently and all of which can be dangerous. They range from materials which are fiercely radioactive for a few minutes to substances which remain mildly radioactive, but highly toxic, for hundreds of thousands of years. It is essential that all of these different radioactive substances are tracked and accounted for throughout their lives, inside and outside the Sellafield site.

The first task of the nuclear power industry pioneers, therefore, was to devise ways of measuring the presence and intensity of the materials they would be handling and to develop ways of protecting themselves – and members of the public – against their effects. Radiation could be measured from the start, although not as accurately as today and certainly not down to the extremely low levels which can be picked up by the sophisticated instruments now available. But then as now it could not be detected by any of the senses, heightening people's fears of the unknown.

Britain's own radiobiological research programme was very small forty years ago and considerable reliance had to be placed on information gleaned with some difficulty from the US, which had carried out large-scale experiments on how various levels of radiation affected animals. From these experiments and from later research, it was established that the various forms of radiation have differing effects on particular parts of the body and that some radioactive materials are easier to protect against than others.

Radioactivity had been discovered in 1896 by a French scientist, Henri Becquerel. He found that pitchblende, which contains uranium and occurs naturally in the earth, could fog photographic plates, even when they were wrapped in black paper, and correctly concluded that some sort of penetrating radiation was at work. It is now known that this radiation consisted of what are called alpha particles and that radioactive materials can also emit two other types of radiation, beta particles and gamma particles. Photographic film is still used to measure external radiation.

Alpha particles are not very penetrating. They can be stopped by a few sheets of paper or a few inches of air. Beta particles are more penetrating, but they can still be stopped by thick cardboard, thin sheets of metal such as aluminium, or a few feet of air. Gamma rays are radiations such as X-rays and they are very penetrating indeed. It takes several inches of metal to reduce gamma radiation to an acceptable level, explaining the need for hospital radiologists to shelter behind protective screens.

The amount of damage caused by radiation depends partly on the particular organs or tissues which are irradiated and partly upon the amount of energy delivered to these tissues by radiation. In addition, certain types of radiation are more damaging than others. Alpha radiation, given off by uranium, plutonium and other elements with atoms heavier than that of uranium, known as transuranics, is somewhat more damaging than the beta or gamma radiation given off by fission products.

Serious injuries and even death can be caused by both internal and external radiation. Internal radiation is usually caused by people inhaling or swallowing radioactive materials or absorbing them through their skin, particularly through cuts and abrasions. If it gets into the body, the radioactive material may eventually bring about various disorders; in some cases the process can take decades. But external radiation can also cause diseases, such as leukaemia, and both forms of radiation can have adverse biological effects by damaging cells, chromosomes and individual genes, producing mutations.

Since the start of the industry, the main way of protecting the workforce from high external radiation has been to ensure that the sources of this radiation are kept behind lead or concrete shielding. All workers at Sellafield are exposed to some external radiation, however. The 'shine' coming off some of the older buildings is enough to make some of the more experienced employees walk past them fairly rapidly. Protection against internal radiation or contamination by radioactive materials is mainly a matter of containing them in suitable structures and maintaining extremely high standards of cleanliness within working areas. But some active and toxic materials, such as plutonium, must be completely enclosed and prevented from reaching employees in even the smallest quantities – an objective which it has not always been possible to achieve.

Protecting the Sellafield workforce against the effect of plutonium is a particular problem, because tiny particles of it can cause considerable damage. Plutonium also tends to stay in the body once it has got there. The health protection agencies therefore set limits not only for how much plutonium a radiation worker can be allowed to receive annually but also how much plutonium can be allowed to accumulate within his or her body, or indeed particular organs, in a lifetime. Once in the body, plutonium collects in a number of organs, but the main dangers from it are lung cancer and leukaemia.

Since they are most exposed, it might have been expected that society's main concern would be with ensuring that the Sellafield employees who work with radioactive materials are properly safeguarded and that there is constant vigilance in this area. But because of the attention paid to the issue by the environmental groups, more emphasis is placed on the small amount of radiation – no more than one-tenth of 1 per cent of the total radiation to which they will be exposed naturally – which reaches members of the public as a result of the nuclear power industry's activities.

All life on earth has been exposed to natural radiation for the whole of the planet's 3,500 million years of evolution. Natural radiation washes over us all every moment of our lives. The average radiation dose received by people living in the UK from naturally occurring sources is about 220 millirems (0.22 rems) a year. The actual amount varies enormously, depending on such factors as altitude, which affects the amount of radiation received from cosmic rays, the nature of the soil or underlying rock in particular areas, the radioactivity in food and some building materials, and even the effectiveness of the insulation in our homes, which can trap radon and thoron, which are radioactive gases. Individual doses in the UK range from 100 millirems to one rem a year.

Natural radiation in the Sellafield area is about the national average. In some areas where there is a lot of granite, such as parts of Scotland and Cornwall, natural radiation levels can be four or five times the national average and in other parts of the world the levels are several times higher than that. In all, naturally occurring background radiation in the UK accounts on average for nearly 87 per cent of the radiation which anyone outside the nuclear industry will ever receive.

Of the remaining 13 per cent, more than 12 per cent comes from medical exposure, mainly from X-rays, 0.4 per cent from the fall-out from weapons tests and the lingering effects of Chernobyl and only 0.1 per cent from routine discharges from nuclear sites. Nevertheless, until the last ten years or so it has been the tiny amount of additional radiation caused by the operations of the nuclear power industry which has dominated the thinking of such organizations as the International Commission for Radiological Protection and the National Radiological Protection Board, which set the safety standards.

Some of my BNFL colleagues were extremely irritated by this at times, arguing that far more lives would be saved if something was done to ensure that houses and buildings containing radon, which accounts for nearly half of the natural radiation in our environment, were properly ventilated or the sources of the gas removed than by any new restrictions placed on discharges of radioactive materials into the general environment by the nuclear power industry. Work is now being carried out to deal with the worst of the radon problem, but it has taken a long time for anything to be done about it.

Taken to its logical conclusion, the concept that there is no safe level of radiation to which the nuclear industry works would lead society to encourage whole populations to move away from areas where there are enhanced levels of natural radiation, to discourage air travel and the sale of Brazil nuts, which are particularly radioactive, and to prohibit activities likely to attract crowds, because of the small amount of extra radiation people get from being in close proximity to each other. That level of interference in civil liberties is impossible to contemplate. It is obvious to me that the real reason so much effort has been put into reducing radioactive emissions from nuclear sites is that it is far easier to do something about that than about providing protection against the sources of natural radiation or changing the habits or habitat of a large part of the population.

In addition to natural radiation, some members of the public, particularly people living near Sellafield, receive considerably more than a 0.1 per cent addition to their total radiation dose. To protect these people – and by inference the rest of the population – the regulators have developed radiation protection standards which are based on monitoring the behaviour of a so-called 'critical group' of people who are not radiation workers but who receive higher than normal doses of radiation as a result of nuclear activities.

In the Sellafield area the critical group consists of a handful of people who are voracious eaters of locally caught fish, which are exposed to radiation from contaminated silt in some of the estuaries close to the factory, who eat locally produced foodstuffs such as milk and vegetables affected by aerial discharges, or who receive gamma radiation emitted directly from the site.

If other minor pathways are included and if someone did all of the things which have to be taken into account, it is just possible that he or she would get an extra forty millirems of radiation each year as a result of Sellafield's operations. When it is in full operation, THORP is expected to add another three millirems or so to this figure. The limit for the total exposure of members of the public from all man-made sources of exposure, excluding medical treatments, is currently set at 100 millirems a year for year-after-year exposure.

About two-thirds of the radiation now reaching the critical group from Sellafield comes from discharges of radioactive materials made in the past rather than today, and there is not much which can be done about that, other than to wait for the radioactivity to decay. By spending more than £2,000 million on waste management and effluent treatment plant, BNFL has succeeded in bringing current discharges from Sellafield down to less than 1 per cent of the peak levels reached in the early 1970s, a considerable achievement.

But it has not been the routine discharges from Sellafield which have caused most disquiet. Rather, it has been the exceptional events, particularly when they have been associated with what could be described as cover-ups. The most notable of these were obviously the 1957 fire and the 1983 Beach Incident, but there have been others.

During the early 1970s discharges of caesium, which is taken up by fish in the Irish Sea, rose nearly twelvefold as a result of the corrosion of the cladding on the spent Magnox fuel in Sellafield's storage ponds. With the cladding breached, considerable quantities of caesium escaped into the pond water and was then discharged to the sea. The critical control subject at that time was assumed to be a member of the coastal fishing community eating 265 grammes a day of locally caught fish – a particularly keen fish eater. Such a person would have reached 44 per cent of the dose limit then in force – and exceeded today's limits.

The caesium problem arose because BNFL was having difficulties with the equipment used to strip the cladding off the spent fuel elements before they are reprocessed. As a result the reprocessing operation had to be slowed down and there was a build-up of spent fuel in the ponds. This increased the pond storage time of the spent fuel and therefore the amount of corrosion which took place, releasing caesium into the pond water. This had to be purged out to sea because of the high radiation levels on site. Just to prove that Murphy's law usually operates in these circumstances, BNFL was also waiting for additional highly active waste storage tanks to be delivered, to hold some of the most dangerous materials separated by reprocessing, and had to slow down reprocessing further when they did not arrive. This was the time of the three-day week in British industry and the tanks were not available.

The electricity utilities of the day, the CEGB and the SSEB, became extremely agitated as the reprocessing rate fell at Sellafield and they were forced to keep spent fuel for longer periods than normal in the storage ponds at their nuclear power stations. This fuel also started to corrode, contaminating their ponds and raising the radiation levels in them, worrying their employees. The problem threatened to force the CEGB, the SSEB and BNFL itself to shut down their Magnox power stations.

Sellafield took some years to work off the backlog of fuel sitting in its own or its customers' ponds. To relieve the situation, one of the Calder Hall reactors was shut down and used as a spent-fuel store for nearly nine months, costing BNFL millions of pounds in lost revenue from electricity sales.

In the end the caesium problem was overcome by the provision of new stripping facilities for Magnox fuel, by containing the spent fuel in pond skips capable of preventing most of the radioactive material leaching out and eventually, in the mid-1980s, by the commissioning of new plant, the most important of which was the site ion exchange effluent plant (SIXEP), which cleans up 4,000 gallons of mildly radioactive water a day before it is sent out to sea.

During the early 1970s Sellafield also had a problem with aerial discharges of radioactive materials. In 1972 the average three-monthly discharge of iodine 131 suddenly shot up, reaching levels which were nearly forty times those experienced normally. It was the release of iodine 131, which attacks the thyroid and to which children are most vulnerable, which led to a ban on milk consumption in the Sellafield area at the time of the 1957 fire. The sharp rise in iodine 131 releases in 1972 was due to the inadvertent reprocessing of spent fuel which had not been cooled long enough before reprocessing – the opposite of the caesium release problem. This was a serious error, although it was expected that the effect of the additional discharge on members of the public would be small.

The Sellafield management always insisted that they learned from their mistakes and usually they did. But short-cooled fuel was reprocessed again during the 1980s because one of the CEGB power stations sent the site fuel which had not been in its ponds for as long as it said. Much to the annoyance of the Sellafield managers, they were blamed by the press for this second error, despite the CEGB's admission of guilt. A new spent fuel management regime was introduced by Sellafield – one which took no account of the time the generating boards said the fuel had resided in their ponds.

These incidents were heavily publicized and made to sound dangerous, even though BNFL insisted that they had led to discharges which were within safety limits and which had caused no harm. People were naturally confused and questioned the validity of the standards recommended by the

International Commission for Radiological Protection and the National Radiological Protection Board and implemented by the Government regulators. They reacted by bringing in the ALARA principle in 1983, by lowering the limits in 1985 and by revising the discharge authorizations in 1986. As a result of all this regulatory activity, it now appeared that Sellafield's discharges were close to the limits instead of well below them, which did nothing to reassure those who were unaware that the earlier limits had been lowered. The new regulations also came in after new clean-up plants were built and so the authorities were criticized for following Sellafield's performance rather than setting the agenda for change.

It would have been pointless and probably dangerous for new limits to be set before Sellafield was capable of meeting them. If the site was incapable of meeting the new discharge targets, it would have had to stop reprocessing – and that would have meant a build-up of spent fuel in the storage ponds and a repeat of the caesium discharge problems of the 1970s. It is also not true that the various protection agencies never take the lead. It is largely at their instigation that the maximum radiation dose levels now accepted by the nuclear industry are far lower than those which applied at the start of the industry or even those in operation twenty years ago, when I first went inside Sellafield.

As far as the workforce is concerned, there has been a reduction in the statutory occupational radiation dose limits from fifteen rems a year in the early 1950s to five rems a year now, and BNFL actually operates a much more restrictive control regime voluntarily, prompted by a report linking childhood cancer to the radiation doses received by their fathers. Although the early fifteen rem control figure now looks far too high, it was exceeded fairly frequently in the early days of the industry, usually as the result of unplanned incidents rather than routine operations.

Despite the best efforts of the regulators, unplanned incidents do and will occur. While I was with the company, there were three accidents involving plutonium, the isotope which causes most concern among the workforce. The first happened in February 1986, when a release of plutonium was detected within the main reprocessing plant. Its source was traced to a pump unit on a sampling line which was under maintenance. Air was accidentally blown across a flow of liquid with plutonium in it, forming a mist which became suspended in the air, a potentially deadly mist. On this occasion I was told about the event fairly quickly. Unfortunately, the information I received, and used to prepare a note to ministers and a press statement, was sparse, inaccurate and kept changing.

I was first told that while non-essential personnel had been evacuated from the affected building, the preliminary indications were that no member of staff was seriously contaminated and that there were no implications for the site or the general public. The following day the message was that assessments continued to show no intake of plutonium by any of the personnel involved and it began to look as though we no longer had a problem.

A day later I heard that tests on the seventy-one employees present in the building at the time of the incident indicated that two men might have breathed in a measurable quantity of plutonium. I was also informed that all of the plutonium had not been contained within the reprocessing plant building after all. A tiny amount, equivalent to two days' normal aerial discharge from the site, had been released into the atmosphere.

A week later further checks indicated that eleven workers might have exceeded the level used by BNFL for further investigation and that one of them might have received as much plutonium from the mist as he was allowed to get in a year. However, we had the sense this time to explain that the amounts of plutonium we were seeking were at the very limit of detection and it was likely to take months of analysing urine and faeces samples before we could confirm whether anyone had been seriously contaminated. It was eventually established that no one had been contaminated beyond the annual limits, but by then the media had lost interest and the all-clear did not get much coverage. The damage to the company's credibility, particularly that of the press officers, had been done.

The second event received no publicity at all because we kept the story under wraps as nothing actually happened. Potentially, however, it was much more serious than the plutonium mist incident. Sellafield's plutonium store contains thousands of cans of plutonium. In 1990 I was informed that routine visual checks had shown that some of these cans were bulging, presumably as a result of the formation of gases inside the containers, and that there was a danger of the cans bursting open. Although there was an element of luck in the way the problem was identified, it was discovered in time and the containers were replaced. But there could have been a very nasty accident.

The third incident happened in September 1992 and once again there was an element of good fortune about the way it was detected. This time a welded joint failed inside a cell where plutonium nitrate solution was being evaporated as part of the reprocessing operation and thirty litres of the muddy green liquid was sprayed on to the floor and walls of the cell. It was spotted by an employee who had the unenviable task of keeping an eye on what was happening inside the cell through a murky observation window made of thick protective glass. I know it was murky because the BNFL board visited the evaporator cell building that month, largely to encourage the workers who had the difficult and dangerous task of clearing up the mess in the cell, spending only a few minutes at a time inside it despite wearing protective suits.

The plutonium had formed into little mounds and it took some time for me to see it through the glass. Neville Chamberlain pointed it out to me. 'Take a good look, Harold. You will never see as much plutonium as that again in your life,' he said. If the plutonium mounds had been in different positions, there would have been a criticality incident – that is, an uncontrolled chain reaction. The workers removing the material had to be careful not to remove the mounds of plutonium in the wrong sequence or they could also have caused an explosion. Another director informed me later that we were lucky we had not been producing military plutonium at the time, as that would have increased the chances of there being a major accident appreciably.

Initially the Sellafield management tried to play down the significance of the event, arguing that as the leak was contained within the cell and there was no off-site impact the incident should be given the lowest classification on the international nuclear event scale. This seven-stage scale runs from 1: Anomaly, through 2: Incident, 3: Serious Incident, 4: Accident without Significant Off-site Risk, 5: Accident with Off-site Risk and 6: Serious Accident to 7: Major Accident. The regulators refused to accept that the event was a mere anomaly, however, and insisted on upgrading it to category 3: Serious Incident, which, because of its potential for disaster, it was.

The plutonium release in the evaporator cell forced BNFL to halt reprocessing. Initially it was thought that the incident would mean a shutdown lasting a few days and that is what we announced publicly. Later we reported that further investigations had shown that it would take a few weeks to recover the liquor and carry out repairs. In the end, it was several months before the Nuclear Installations Inspectorate allowed Sellafield to start reprocessing again. Substantial work had to be carried out, including the installation of an automatic monitoring system which would go into alarm if there was any further leak within the cell. The job of peering through a murky window for signs of trouble was done away with.

Normally, I am glad to say, the more toxic materials such as plutonium and highly radioactive fission products are handled only remotely, within specially ventilated glove boxes or by workers wearing Windscale suits, the plastic garments with their own air supply which look like space suits and which are often shown in television programmes about Sellafield. The air circulating in all operating buildings has to be monitored continuously for radioactivity and anyone entering a place where radioactive materials are contained must wear a film badge which measures the amount of radioactivity they receive. Records must be kept on the total radiation received by radiation workers and other frequent visitors to the active areas to ensure that dose limits are not exceeded.

Some radiation workers have died from cancers known to have radiation as one of their causes and their dependants have sought compensation from BNFL. When I joined the company, this could be done only by using the processes of law. During the late 1970s five of these cases almost reached the courts after lengthy negotiations had failed to lead to settlements. Each time this happened I had to be on hand at the High Court in Carlisle to deal with the press, radio and television. Without exception, these cases were settled out of court on the eve of the hearings. When it came to the moment of decision, neither the company nor the trade unions supporting the dependants wanted to risk unfortunate legal precedents being set in a complicated area of medical science.

One of the main problems in trying to establish whether radiation has led to a particular cancer is that there are almost invariably other possible causes. In fact, about a third of the total UK population develops a spontaneous cancer at some time in their lives and some three-quarters of these cancers lead to death. It is rarely, if ever, possible to distinguish by medical examination between cancers caused by radiation and those arising from other causes. Accordingly, it is possible to reach a judgement based only on the balance of probabilities. The real issue for BNFL and for the dependants and their legal and trade union advisers was whether they were prepared to accept a High Court judge as expert in this matter or, if not, who they would accept.

In none of the cases which nearly reached the courts was there absolute certainty as to the cause of death, although some cases were obviously stronger than others. The courts cannot cope with uncertainty, however. They operate on an 'all or nothing' basis, where the winner takes all. If they judged that there was a greater than 50 per cent probability that radiation caused the cancer, compensation would be awarded. If they decided that there was less than a 50 per cent chance, the dependant would get nothing. Neither side regarded this situation as satisfactory.

When I worked for the *Financial Times*, I had written several stories about the coal industry's compensation scheme for miners suffering or dying from such diseases as pneumoconiosis. From time to time the Coal Board issued figures covering the number of settlements made under the scheme, which ran into many thousands, but as the diseases were so prevalent at that time very little interest was taken in the Coal Board's regular announcements or in the fate of the thousands of miners affected. The coal dust related diseases were regarded as a routine occupational hazard. After I had stood on the steps of the Carlisle courts building a couple of times, waiting for nothing to happen, I began to ask why BNFL could not introduce a compensation scheme similar to that operated by the Coal Board, but linked of course to radiation-induced diseases.

Several other people at BNFL were beginning to think along the same lines, notably Donald Avery, Peter Mummery and my predecessor as Company Secretary, Arthur Scott, an extremely kind and humane man who had personnel as one of his many responsibilities at the time, as I did later. A compensation scheme would have many advantages for the company and for its workforce. The simple reduction of legal fees meant that the company could afford to be more generous towards those making claims for compensation. It could also make payments on a sliding scale, beginning at a probability as low as 25 per cent of radiation having caused death, right up to full payment at 50 per cent probability and above.

Further advantages were that it should be possible to reach settlements more quickly and that the introduction of a compensation scheme would enable dependants, usually widows, to avoid the harrowing experience of making their claims in the glare of publicity. There was invariably a lot of publicity about potential court cases, as well as extensive media interest on the day of the hearing, and the avoidance of this sort of media exposure was no bad thing for the company either. By refusing to admit liability for causing the death of its employees, even when full compensation was paid out of court, BNFL had appeared to be heartless and just a little pig-headed.

One day, standing outside the courts building in the centre of Carlisle with Bill Maxwell, then the shop stewards' convenor at Sellafield, as we waited to be interviewed about the latest out-of-court settlement, I decided to bring the matter to a head. While we had been doing a lot of talking internally about the possibility of bringing in a compensation scheme, it seemed to me that nothing was actually happening. I talked to Bill about what was going on and when I was interviewed by the BBC and Border Television, I announced that the company intended to begin talks with its trade unions about ways of developing a scheme. By agreement, Bill welcomed my statement when his turn came to appear before the cameras. I half expected to get taken to task for committing the company in this way without prior approval, but Con Allday and his board colleagues agreed that it was time to start negotiating.

But the rest of the nuclear industry was furious with BNFL for selling the pass, as they saw it, and we came under considerable pressure to drop the idea. It is to the credit of the board that it refused to do so and to the credit of those then in power at the Department of Energy that they allowed the company to fulfil my promise to Bill Maxwell. In the event, it took nearly three years to agree the terms of the scheme, which came into force in 1982 and was initially limited to cases where a cancer had caused death. In 1987 the UKAEA joined the scheme and the agreement was extended to include cases where cancer has developed but not caused death.

When the BNFL compensation scheme was launched, the company was forced to state that it was an experiment, in order to placate the rest of the nuclear industry, which was still bitterly opposed to it. By the end of 1995, however, all of the nuclear interests had joined the scheme, the last being the Ministry of Defence. Those of us who played some part in bringing the compensation scheme into being in 1982, particularly Donald Avery and Peter Mummery, who worked on the mechanics of the scheme, have been vindicated.

Even though the BNFL scheme has been expanded into an industry-wide agreement and several thousand cancer deaths have occurred among radiation workers employed in the nuclear industry, the number of awards made under the scheme is relatively small. By the end of 1994 around 500 claims had been received and more than forty payments involving BNFL employees had been made. Radiation-induced cancer is still a rare phenomenon and a relatively small occupational hazard – and should become even rarer as radiation doses are reduced.

My belief that the health of radiation workers employed at Sellafield has been well protected was confirmed by the London School of Hygiene and Tropical Medicine at the end of 1994. Research workers there evaluated the cancer risks up to 1988 among all 14,000 radiation workers employed at the plant from its opening in 1947 up until 1976. Overall, the death rate from all causes combined among the workers was 2 per cent less than that of the general population of England and Wales and 6 per cent less than that of residents of Cumbria.

The cancer death rate was 4 per cent less than that of the national death rate and the same as that of residents of Cumbria. If non-fatal cancers were included, the cancer rate among Sellafield workers was 10 per cent less than that of England and Wales and 18 per cent less than that of the northern region. Those are very reassuring statistics, even though the research team did identify an association between radiation and leukaemia.

Barely a year after establishing its compensation scheme for employees, public attention switched to the off-site effects of Sellafield's activities again when BNFL was faced with the allegation that radioactive materials discharged from the site had caused the death of children living nearby. The claim came in a Yorkshire Television programme, *Windscale: the Nuclear Laundry*, which was largely based on research commissioned by Greenpeace and information provided by a local doctor. The programme went out nationally on Tuesday 1 November 1983, and the facts which it revealed came as a complete surprise to BNFL.

We were not happy about the research methods used by Yorkshire Television in the preparation of this programme and there were complaints about intrusion by members of the public, for which YTV apologized. The fact remains, however, that the programme-makers, led by the producer, James Cutler, uncovered a mystery which has still not been solved, despite a considerable amount of research activity over the last eleven years. BNFL had always been led to believe by the regional health authorities that the incidence of leukaemia and other cancers which can be caused by radiation in west Cumbria was about the national average. What YTV did was to concentrate on coastal villages in west Cumbria, particularly Seascale, two miles south of Sellafield, where many of the site's employees live. They discovered a cluster of leukaemias in these villages and alleged that it might have been caused by discharges of radioactive materials from Sellafield. The incidence of cancer among children and young people was said by YTV to be ten times that expected, although the total number of deaths was so small that there was some argument at first over whether the phenomenon could be regarded as statistically significant. In the end it was agreed that the discovery by YTV was significant and a real cause for concern and the Government set up an independent inquiry to look into the allegations, chaired by Sir Douglas Black.

The Yorkshire Television programme was a brilliant piece of painstaking detective work by the programme's producers and collaborators and deservedly won several television awards. It set in train a major Government inquiry and over a dozen new pieces of academic research which have kept Sellafield in the medical, legal and media spotlights for over a decade. It may also have led to the diversion of research resources which would have been better expended elsewhere.

The advisory group led by Sir Douglas Black reported in December 1985 and gave only qualified reassurance to the people who were concerned about a possible health hazard in the neighbourhood of Sellafield. It concluded that the mortality rate in the whole of west Cumbria was near to the national average (which everybody knew) but went on to say that this did not preclude the existence of local pockets of high incidence (which YTV had already shown). The group recommended that further research should be carried out, including four separate epidemiological studies into various aspects of the problem identified by Yorkshire Television.

One of these studies was carried out by a team led by the late Professor Martin Gardner, of the Medical Research Council's Environmental Epidemiology Unit at the University of Southampton. His objective was to examine whether the observed excess of childhood leukaemia and lymphoma near the Sellafield nuclear plant was associated with established risk factors or with factors related to the plant. The study team examined a total of fifty-two cases of leukaemia, twenty-two of non-Hodgkin's lymphoma and twenty-three of Hodgkin's disease in people under the age of twenty-five years who were born in the West Cumbria Health Authority area between 1950 and 1985. It compared these cases with 1,001 controls taken from the same birth registers into which the cases were entered.

A few days before the Gardner Report was due to be

published, Dr Roger Berry, who had joined the company less than six months earlier to take over from Peter Mummery on his retirement, came to see me. Dr Berry had previously been Professor of Oncology in the Middlesex School of Medicine of University College, London, and was a member of several national and international scientific bodies, but not particularly well versed in the ways of large companies. He told me that he had received a copy of the Gardner Report on a confidential basis and could therefore not give me any details, although he was sure it would lead to considerable national interest. I pressed him hard, but he would not tell me any more, leaving me powerless to do more than put the Press Office on general alert. I felt impotent – and annoyed.

I did learn from Roger Berry that the Gardner Report was to be launched at a London press conference on Thursday 15 February 1990, however, and argued with him that he should try to persuade Professor Gardner to present it in Cumbria and preferably to do so only after speaking to the Sellafield workforce, which had cooperated in the Gardner study. I do not know whether Roger spoke to Professor Gardner or not, but the London press conference went ahead as planned. I had less than forty-eight hours' notice of what the report contained and was forbidden to speak to the workforce by the terms of the embargo placed on it.

The Gardner Report's main finding was that the external radiation received by fathers during their employment at Sellafield was associated with the development of leukaemia among their children. It suggested that men who received more than ten rems of radiation before the date of their child's conception, especially if they had been exposed to one rem or more in the six months prior to conception, stood six to eight times the chance of fathering a child with leukaemia than other men. The indications were that radiation exposures at these levels affected the germ cells of the workers concerned, producing a mutation in their sperm which led to leukaemia in their children.

It was the stuff of nightmares, made worse by the fact that the Sellafield workforce first heard about it through the media. They had to face up to headlines speaking of 'Sellafield's Deadly Inheritance' or stating as fact that 'Dads Passed Cancer to Babies'. Some of the employees who had children with leukaemia were in despair and the company was suddenly faced with thousands of worried families seeking advice, comfort and reassurance. And although most radiation workers are men, some women had dose records too, including at least one pregnant woman, and they were worried that there might be some mechanism by which they could also pass on leukaemia to their children.

Sellafield was in turmoil as thousands of workers and former employees tried to find out what the Gardner theory meant to them. One of the company doctors counselling members of the workforce at this time had to be taken off the job because of his own deep concerns and the effect which talking to hundreds of anxious people was having on him.

The Gardner hypothesis was totally unexpected. No one had ever suggested before that childhood leukaemia was linked to paternal employment at Sellafield, although there were plenty of other theories. To the contrary, the only other relevant data available was that related to studies involving the 7,400 children of Japanese men who survived the atomic bomb explosions. These showed no hint of an increased risk of leukaemia in the offspring, but Gardner had an explanation for this too. He suggested that as the radiation doses in Hiroshima and Nagasaki were instantaneous, rather than accumulated over a period of years, as in the case of the Sellafield workers, the different dose rates might be important. Another possibility was that internal rather than external radiation exposure was relevant. The Gardner hypothesis was based on very small numbers – only ten cases of leukaemia over a period of thirty-six years, from 1950 to 1985 – and it is a sad fact that around 1,200 children develop leukaemia every year in the UK. But those ten cases attracted more attention than all the others put together.

Despite the conflicting indicators, the BNFL board was advised by Roger Berry that he believed the Gardner hypothesis was founded on sound science and was personally convinced that the link with radiation exposure to the fathers had been proved, even if it had not been established as a medical fact. With so little advance notice of what the Gardner Report contained, all BNFL could do when it was launched at that London press conference was to promise to take the report extremely seriously and review all of the implications for the health and safety of its employees and their families. Dr Berry also arranged for Professor Gardner to go up to Sellafield to discuss his hypothesis with the workforce. It was somewhat late in the day in my view, but the meeting went ahead on Wednesday 21 February in one of Sellafield's largest indoor meeting areas, which was packed.

Far from helping the situation, the meeting led to even more trouble for BNFL. Immediately after it ended Professor Gardner held a news conference, supported by Roger Berry and others. I was not there but received an urgent phone call from Jeffrey Preece, BNFL's Director of Information, to say that Dr Berry had told the media that the company was considering advising its Sellafield employees not to have families, in order to avoid the risk of fathering a child with leukaemia. The words actually used by Dr Berry were these: 'It may be that the proper advice is, if you are so worried, then maybe the advice is that you do not have a family.'

Jeffrey told me that the story was about to go out on the Press Association news agency service. I asked to speak to Roger Berry to clarify the situation but was informed that he had left Sellafield. I decided that BNFL had to distance itself from Dr Berry's statement. I did not believe that the company could operate the Sellafield site if it could do so only by asking most of its workforce to stay celibate or use contraceptives – or by the company establishing a sperm bank or calling for radiation volunteers among the older men, two other worrying suggestions made by Dr Berry internally. So I immediately put out a statement to the effect that what Dr Berry had apparently said was not company policy. I went on to say that BNFL had promised a programme of medical counselling by the factory doctors for all employees at Sellafield who wished it, on an individual basis, with the aim of ensuring that they understood what the Gardner Report was saying and what the risk might be to them if its conclusions were confirmed.

'Ultimately it is then for each individual worker to reach a decision, not for the company to advise on one course of action or another. If an individual worker requested to be moved to a different area of work to reduce his radiation exposure, the company would give sympathetic consideration to the request,' I said. Once again I had been forced to make company policy on the run, as it were, under the pressure of media interest. There was no time to consult anyone or to get approval.

The press saw my statement as the company disowning its Director of Health and Safety and that is probably a fair assessment of what I did. But I honestly believed that I was protecting not only BNFL but the career of Roger Berry. I did not see how he could continue in his post if his implied policy statement was allowed to stay on the record. I know that he never accepted this and felt let down. I am sorry for that. He was pilloried by some of the tabloids, which somehow found out where he lived and camped outside his home in Cheshire, waiting for him to return from Sellafield that night. Roger and his wife, Valerie, do not have children and this became known too, and one of the papers tried to link this to the advice about not fathering children which Roger had given. I have been 'door-stepped' by journalists myself and know what a rotten experience it is and I can therefore sympathize with Roger and Val Berry. But my main sympathies were with the Sellafield workforce.

Some of the workforce tried to make light of the Gardner

theory, a not uncommon defence mechanism. One of the shop stewards met a member of my staff at a conference and asked her whether she had heard what had caused the unexplained leukaemias at Seascale. Tapping the crotch of his trousers, he said, 'It's in the jeans.' To some that may seem a sick play on words. To me it sounded more like a cry of despair.

Following the Roger Berry episode, the trade unions stepped up their pressure on the company to decide what it was going to do, rightly making the point that waiting for the results of further research was no answer to the immediate problem of a workforce which had been completely stunned and demoralized by the Gardner hypothesis. Jack Dromey, of the Transport and General Workers Union, was particularly incensed at what he saw as the company's lack of action and warned that some trade union members were threatening to stop work.

Matters were brought to a head on Friday 23 February 1990, when the trade unions demanded a meeting with Neville Chamberlain. Fortuitously, Mr Chamberlain, Roger Berry, Grahame Smith, the Sellafield site director, and I were at the Hilton Hotel, near Manchester Airport, for a senior management group conference. The four of us sat round the table and discussed what we were going to say to the trade union leaders, whom Neville had agreed to meet at the Heathrow business centre that afternoon – and, far more importantly, what we were going to do about the Gardner Report. I told Neville Chamberlain that in my view it did not matter what reservations we might have about the Gardner hypothesis – and we had plenty – we had no alternative but to treat it as though it was correct. To do otherwise would mean that we were prepared to tell our employees, and not just the Sellafield workforce, that if they continued to work for the company they would have to take the chance of fathering children with leukaemia.

I maintained that radiation doses had to be brought down

to the levels which Gardner appeared to be saying were safe. Grahame Smith opposed this view. He said that he did not believe the Gardner theory and that the cost of reducing radiation doses as much as the Gardner Report indicated was necessary would ruin the reprocessing business. I stood my ground and pointed out that the costing exercise had not been done. It was appearing to ignore Gardner which would damage reprocessing, as we could be in for a long drawn out strike which would be ended only by some action on dose reduction.

Neville Chamberlain agreed with my analysis and asked me to accompany him to the meeting he had arranged with the unions. He also asked me to draft a statement which we could seek to agree with them. When Neville and I arrived at Heathrow off the Manchester shuttle, we were greeted by the BBC and ITV cameras and a dozen or so journalists. We promised them that we would make a statement after we had met the unions and went into the meeting with an agitated group of trade union officials. It was immediately apparent that Jack Dromey, married to Harriet Harman, MP, and with young children of his own, was very upset about what the Gardner Report contained and about what Roger Berry had said. He had to be calmed down by Jimmy Airley, the Chairman of the trade union side of the Company Joint Industrial Council, before it was agreed that the statement I had drafted should be used as the focus for our discussion.

I put several proposals on the table, all of which were agreed. The most important of these was that we should prepare a joint programme aimed at ensuring that no worker received more than one and a half rems of radiation a year. This would ensure that no one received more than one rem in six months, the pre-conception guideline contained in the Gardner Report. BNFL also agreed to commission a case control study on leukaemia incidence among children in west Cumbria in comparison with other areas in the north of England and to make all relevant information available to any other inquiries. If further research work substantiated the Gardner hypothesis, the company would immediately discuss with employee representatives ways in which it could discharge its duties as a caring employer determined to look after the well-being of its employees and their families. This would include discussion of ways of mitigating the effects of the disease, ways in which its causes could be identified and eliminated, and a compensation formula.

The journalists waiting to interview us when the meeting broke up had clearly expected a confrontation and possibly an announcement from the unions that they were calling a strike. Instead they learned of the positive steps we would be taking together to bring radiation dose levels down, by introducing new plant, by better shielding of older plant and by the employment of more radiation workers, so that exposure could be shared across a larger working population.

At that time no fewer than 285 of the 6,500 radiation workers at Sellafield received doses above the one and a half rems a year level, so the task of bringing radiation dose levels down was not going to be easy. Nevertheless, by 1994 only four people received radiation doses of more than one and a half rems, a tremendous achievement. It is arguable whether such a drastic reduction was necessary, but there are a lot of people sleeping easier in their beds in west Cumbria now.

As a result of the Gardner Report, the statutory regulations were strengthened. In addition to the statutory dose limit of five rems, an investigation now has to take place when an employee's annual dose exceeds one and a half rems and the Health and Safety Executive introduced a further investigation level to apply when an employee receives a cumulative dose of more than seven and a half rems in any five-year period. The purpose of both these investigations is to see what can be done to reduce such doses in the future. And BNFL has gone even further by adopting voluntary dose restriction levels of two rems a year and seven and a half rems over five years.

When it was first put forward, the Gardner theory appeared

to provide the answers to the questions most asked by the parents of the dead children or of children still suffering the agonies of leukaemia. Why has this happened to my child? Why has it happened to me? Why should the people who have caused this to happen get away with it? No parents wanted to believe, or could believe, that their children were the victims of random chance. They wanted to blame someone or something – and Sellafield was at hand.

A solicitor who had taken a particular interest in radiation effects, Martyn Day, had advertised for people who thought Sellafield might have caused leukaemias to come forward. More than forty potential cases were identified by him as a result of this campaign and it seemed at first that he would argue in court that radioactive discharges from Sellafield had caused the leukaemias. On the publication of the Gardner Report Mr Day made the assertions contained in that the main plank of his legal argument.

He obtained legal aid and notified BNFL that he intended to go ahead with two cases. Dorothy Reay died from leukaemia in September 1962 aged ten months. Her father, George Reay, was a fitter at Sellafield from 1949 to 1977 and died in 1987 after a twelve-year fight against stomach cancer. According to his seventy-three-year-old widow, Mrs Elizabeth Reay, who sued BNFL for £150,000 damages, compensation for the loss of her daughter and the anguish caused to her and her late husband, Mr Reay had died believing that his daughter's death had been caused by something he had given her from Sellafield.

The other case involved Miss Vivien Hope, aged twenty-eight. She lived in Seascale and in 1988 fell ill with non-Hodgkin's lymphoma, which attacked her glands, kidneys and spine. After an operation to remove tumours from her spine, she was left in a wheelchair. By remarkable willpower, Miss Hope cast off her illness, her wheelchair and her walking sticks to return to work at Sellafield as a clerical assistant. 'The truth is there is nowhere else to work around here,' she told the press. Miss Hope also became sterile after receiving chemotherapy as part of her treatment. Her father, David, had worked at Sellafield for thirty-three years until his retirement in 1988, first as a fitter and then as an inspector. It was the publication of the Gardner Report which prompted Miss Hope to wonder if her father had somehow been responsible for her near-fatal illness and she sued BNFL for £125,000 damages for personal injury.

When it appeared that Martyn Day intended to argue that radioactive discharges had caused cancer, the BNFL board was in no doubt that it must defend any actions he brought. But when he claimed that the cause was parental pre-conception irradiation, as identified by Professor Gardner, the board was less sure. It fell to me, as Company Secretary, to advise the board on whether we should continue to contest the claims brought against the company by Mrs Reay and Miss Hope. I came to the conclusion that BNFL still had to defend its position as vigorously as possible, for two reasons. If we truly believed that the Gardner hypothesis was wrong, which nearly all of us did by then, even Roger Berry, we should be prepared to challenge it through the courts, however heartless that might make us seem. I also felt that if we settled out of court, it would appear that we considered it acceptable to cause childhood leukaemia and then buy off the problem for what would be regarded as peanuts to a company with BNFL's £1,000 million turnover. I did not believe that there was a future for the business if we took that stance. It might have been cheaper to settle, although Mr Day claimed to have another forty or more cases waiting to be brought forward if the two test cases succeeded, but I convinced the board that there were important principles at stake which should not be sacrificed. They agreed that we had to fight the cases brought by Mrs Reay and Miss Hope, portrayed as two frail women heroically taking on the might of BNFL.

They did so, of course, at the expense of the state, because Mr Day had secured legal aid. BNFL eventually spent over

£10 million on defending the two cases, including the cost of legal fees, witness expenses and the massive amount of research and preparation which had to be carried out by BNFL Legal and Health and Safety Directorate staff. And, as BNFL is state-owned, that was ultimately at the expense of the state as well. It was an expensive way to test a statistical hypothesis.

In October 1993, BNFL was cleared in the High Court of causing cancers in Dorothy Reay and Vivien Hope. Announcing his verdict, Mr Justice French said that the Gardner hypothesis stood alone, unsupported by other studies. He also said that criticism of the Gardner theory by BNFL's witnesses all had validity and diminished confidence in its conclusions. This served to underline the good sense of requiring that studies such as that carried out by Professor Gardner should be confirmed by at least one other study of the same or similar subject matter before reliance was placed on its results.

'I have considered with care all arguments advanced on behalf of the plaintiffs,' Mr Justice French said. 'That which has given me the greatest cause for pause and reflection is the argument that if causality through parental pre-conception irradiation (PPI) is not the explanation, then the fact that the Seascale excess is fathered by "high dose" cases must be due to chance, an explanation which, of course, the plaintiffs urge me to reject. In my judgement, however, on the evidence before me, the scales tilt decisively in favour of the defendants and the plaintiffs, therefore, have failed to satisfy me on the balance of probability that PPI was a material contributory cause of the Seascale excess or, it must follow, of (a) the leukaemia of Dorothy Reay or (b) the non-Hodgkin's lymphoma of Vivien Hope.'

I had left BNFL by the time these cases ended, but I can understand my former colleagues' sense of relief at the verdict reached in the High Court, supported in May 1994 when follow-on cases were struck out at Maidstone Crown Court. Nevertheless, no one would argue that research into the phenomenon of the Seascale childhood leukaemia cluster must continue, even if the Gardner hypothesis is now largely discounted as the explanation.

The theory gaining most support currently is one put forward by another researcher, Dr Leo Kinlen, long before the Gardner hypothesis gained currency. He had argued that a sudden influx of outside workers into an area, taking with them an as yet unidentified virus or other agent might be the trigger for the leukaemia clusters. In his most recent study, published in 1995, Dr Kinlen examined what had happened at large construction sites imposed on rural communities, such as greenfield sites for power stations and refineries, in much the same way that Sellafield was planted in west Cumbria.

When the wider area around Sellafield was studied like this – rather than concentrating on the single village of Seascale – it fell into a common pattern with other greenfield construction sites and showed a mildly elevated risk of leukaemia. Building on that, Dr Kinlen's explanation for the cluster which occurred at Seascale is that it was the result of the village experiencing a uniquely high population movement and mixing pattern, as managers were moved into and out of the areas by BNFL and the UKAEA. Seascale has also always had an exceptionally high proportion of white-collar workers and other researchers have already established that higher social class and better living standards are additional risk factors for the occurrence of childhood leukaemia cases.

The Kinlen hypothesis appears to rule out the likelihood of radiation being responsible for the leukaemia cluster at Seascale and that is obviously good news for BNFL. But it is still a hypothesis. It would be just as wrong for BNFL or anyone else to grab at this explanation for what happened in west Cumbria as it was for others to treat Professor Gardner's theory as if it was fact. More research is needed – and not only into the Kinlen hypothesis.

Chapter Six

The Objectors:

War and Greenpeace

Opposition to military and civil nuclear power took a surprisingly long time to get going in Britain, despite the horrific pictures which came out of Hiroshima and Nagasaki in 1945. CND was not even formed until thirteen years after the first atomic bomb was dropped by the US and seven years after plutonium from Sellafield was used in Britain's own first atomic weapon test at Monte Bello in Australia. Support for Britain retaining the nuclear deterrent has remained firm, although that may change as people look for tangible evidence of the peace dividend which the ending of the Cold War was supposed to bring. A rather more successful campaign has been waged against civil nuclear power, a softer target. It was initially led by Friends of the Earth, although Greenpeace makes most of the running today, but it took a highly critical report by the Royal Commission on Environmental Pollution, published in September 1976, to give the campaign its early impetus and credibility.

I have already described the impact which this influential

report had on nuclear waste management and disposal policy, but it also made a considerable contribution to the debate on the political, social and ethical issues raised by civil nuclear power, particularly reprocessing and the separation of plutonium at Sellafield, which was just getting under way. The report appeared shortly before the THORP public inquiry began and not long after I had joined the nuclear industry – an impeccable piece of timing. It came like a kick in the teeth to Con Allday and my other new colleagues at BNFL as we prepared to do battle for planning permission for THORP.

The Royal Commission consisted of seventeen eminent people drawn from among the great and the good, including a leavening of noted scientists, and its Chairman was considered to be one of the nuclear industry's own, Sir Brian (later Lord) Flowers, Rector of Imperial College and a part-time member of the UKAEA, where one of his colleagues was Con Allday, my new Chief Executive. The Royal Commission's views could not be shrugged off as the fevered ravings of people with vivid imaginations and suspect political motives – the nuclear industry's customary response to opposition in those days.

The Flowers Report was quick to identify the basic problem with the nuclear debate called for by Tony Benn. Flowers suspected that because of the range and difficulty of the issues raised by nuclear power, the debate would serve only to polarize the views of those who were for and those who were against nuclear power, rather than lead to reconciliation. Unfortunately, time has proved him right. A decade or more later, I was involved with Sir Christopher Harding, then Chairman of BNFL, in an attempt to build bridges between the company and Friends of the Earth and Greenpeace, but try as we might we failed to find any common ground.

As the Royal Commission said in 1976, so it is today. The proponents of nuclear power still see its development as inevitable if the world's longer-term energy needs are to be met. They are convinced that its hazards have been or can be reduced by technical and other safeguards to a level where, because of the benefits, they should be accepted. The opponents of nuclear power development see it as something fraught with danger for mankind, to be avoided by seeking alternative and less dangerous sources of energy, or even by accepting restraints in energy use – and if that means significant changes in the approach we take towards economic growth, so be it.

At the time the Royal Commission began its study in the mid-1970s, there were only about 200 commercial nuclear reactors in operation in some twenty countries world-wide, but the forecasts of growth were truly awe-inspiring. The number of reactors expected to be in operation by the mid-1980s was about 500 in more than thirty countries and by the year 2000 the total installed nuclear capacity throughout the world was thought likely to be equivalent to operating 6,000 nuclear power stations of the size then in use.

As far as the UK was concerned, projections of growth indicated a twentyfold increase by the year 2000 and a further quadrupling of capacity by the year 2030. An indicative programme used by the UKAEA for its research and development planning purposes had UK nuclear electrical generating capacity rising from 5,000 megawatts to 104,000 megawatts by the year 2000 and to no less than 426,000 megawatts by the year 2030. (In the event, total generating capacity in the UK today amounts to only 70,000 megawatts, of which some 13,000 megawatts is nuclear.) On the UKAEA scenario of the mid-1970s there was to be extremely rapid growth in the use of plutonium burning and producing fast-breeder reactors in the later years of the programme, and by the year 2030 it was thought that fast breeders would constitute the main source of nuclear electricity, with a staggering capacity of 370,000 megawatts.

By 2030 the UKAEA thought it possible that there would be several hundred large nuclear reactors in operation in Britain and, depending on the siting policy adopted, that these reactors would be installed in perhaps 100 nuclear stations on coastal sites scattered throughout the country. To fuel this vast expansion of the fast reactor programme would require a huge increase in the production and separation of plutonium. Plutonium production would have to increase from a little over ten tonnes in 1975 to about 250 tonnes in the year 2000 and perhaps 2,500 tonnes by the year 2030, according to the UKAEA. There would also be a substantial movement of plutonium between different nuclear facilities, incorporated in new fuel elements.

And this was only what was expected to happen in Britain. Predictions of world growth in nuclear capacity indicated that by the year 2000 the installed nuclear generating capacity might approach 3 million megawatts – about thirty times the figure projected by the UKAEA for the UK alone. The US was expected to see the biggest growth, as one would expect. There it was estimated that by the year 2000 there might be the equivalent of 2,000 large reactors in operation, most of them fast-breeder reactors; that there might be about sixty fuel reprocessing and fabrication plants at work; that plutonium generation might exceed 30,000 tonnes in total; and that, assuming a dispersed industry, about 100,000 shipments of plutonium might have to take place annually.

'Such proliferation of reactors, nuclear plants and shipments of nuclear materials throughout the world will certainly greatly increase the probability of accidents and the opportunities for malevolence,' the Flowers Report said, fuelling the fears of the burgeoning anti-nuclear movement. The Royal Commission pointed out that at that time, ignoring the quantities of plutonium produced for weapons programmes, not much more than ten tonnes of plutonium had been created in the UK and perhaps an order of magnitude more in the whole world. Nuclear development on the scale indicated by the UKAEA would create a new situation in which plutonium, notwithstanding its dangers, would be in widespread use as a staple commodity of energy supply. It would lead to what was already being called 'the plutonium economy'.

With so much plutonium expected to be on the move, the Flowers Report raised the terrifying spectre of a police state having to be created to protect it. To the considerable annoyance of the nuclear industry, the Royal Commission came to the conclusion that 'plutonium appears to offer unique and terrifying potential for threat and blackmail against society' and was deeply concerned about its potential attraction to terrorists or criminal organizations.

This threat has not so far materialized, although it is still there, probably more so now with considerable stocks of plutonium being held by impoverished countries within the former USSR. One reason for theft, the value of the element as an energy resource, has diminished with the failure of the world-wide nuclear programme to take off, but the other, its potential use as a terrorist weapon – including international terrorism by less politically stable countries – remains.

The Royal Commission maintained that it was not even necessary for terrorists to know how to make an atomic bomb from their stolen plutonium. They could use conventional explosives to disseminate it into the atmosphere, where it would not only pose long-term radiological hazards to those who inhaled the airborne particles but also contaminate large areas of land, which could be decontaminated only at vast expense. The Flowers Report also acknowledged – for the first time from such an authoritative source – that there was a real risk of an illicit group constructing a nuclear bomb from civil-grade plutonium and pointed out that the amount of plutonium needed to make such a bomb might be as low as four kilogrammes.

The problems of safeguarding society against threats and blackmail from groups obtaining plutonium illicitly could become formidable in a 'plutonium economy', the Royal Commission warned. There were particular risks during the transport of plutonium between nuclear installations, although ways might be found to make access to the plutonium both dangerous and difficult. There was also the risk of theft of plutonium by direct action at installations where it was stored or even by people working in the nuclear industry. To counteract that, it might be necessary to create special security organizations, which would need to exercise unprecedented thoroughness and vigilance in order to safeguard the material while significant quantities remained on earth in accessible form.

In the US, Alvin Weinberg was gaining support for his view that the necessary vigilance and continuity could not be guaranteed in any normal organization. He thought that it might be necessary to establish a 'nuclear priesthood' – a dedicated, self-perpetuating body of people forming a technological élite which would be entrusted through the generations with the task of safeguarding society from the hazards of nuclear power. While the idea of such a 'priesthood' might be far-fetched, the fact that it took hold showed the extent of the anxiety which responsible people were starting to show about the potential hazards of nuclear power.

An effective security organization could not be merely passive, reacting to events, the Royal Commission argued. It would need to have an active role, infiltrating potentially dangerous organizations, monitoring the activities of nuclear employees and members of the public and generally carrying out clandestine operations. It would also need to have powers of search and powers to clear whole areas in an emergency. Such operations might need to be conducted on a scale greatly exceeding what would otherwise be required on grounds of national security in democratic countries.

According to the Flowers Report:

> The fear is expressed that adequate security against nuclear threats will be obtained only at the price of gradual but inexorable infringements of personal freedom. We are sufficiently persuaded by the dangers of a plutonium economy

> that we regard this as a central issue in the debate over the future of nuclear power. We believe that we should not rely for something as basic as energy on a process that produces such hazardous substances as plutonium unless we are convinced that there is no reasonably certain economic alternative.

Because the scale of the plutonium economy feared by the Royal Commission has not materialized, it is easy now for the nuclear industry to dismiss its predictions of what might need to be done to safeguard plutonium as unnecessary scaremongering. But some of its underlying concerns were shared by some of my colleagues at the time and they have been revived now that THORP is operating at Sellafield, separating out plutonium which is owned by electricity utilities in Europe, Japan and – if BNFL is successful in its current reprocessing sales drive there – South Korea too. On current contractual arrangements some thirty tonnes of plutonium recovered from spent fuel in the first ten years of THORP's operation have to be returned to the thirty customers in nine countries who own them.

The Royal Commission was distinctly uneasy about this, maintaining that the use of plutonium as a potential terrorist threat would be particularly great if it were shipped back to the countries of origin as a pure compound and stating it should be mandatory that plutonium would be returned only in the form of fuel elements produced from a mixture of uranium and plutonium. If this happened, any terrorist group would have to carry out a form of reprocessing in order to gain access to the plutonium – itself difficult and providing more time for detection. Unfortunately, in my view, the recommendation was not accepted and although BNFL is encouraging its customers to accept plutonium back in the form of MOX, with some success, they do not have to do so.

I had an early indication from some of my colleagues that the terrorist threat was regarded by them as a real one. In

April 1976, shortly after Tony Benn had announced that BNFL might take on further reprocessing work for overseas customers but before THORP had been approved, Friends of the Earth chartered a special train to take over 1,000 of its supporters from London to Sellafield to stage an Easter weekend protest. It was the first time most of them had been anywhere near the place and we were not sure what to expect. As the big day approached, there was something close to panic within the BNFL ranks at the site. What if these people broke through the security fence? What if they were infiltrated by IRA terrorists? How could the company keep them away from the more 'sensitive' buildings on the site, such as the plutonium store? What if our own employees, seeing their jobs under threat, turned nasty and had a go at them?

I told the senior managers at Sellafield and my public relations colleagues that they must stop being so defensive and treat the Friends of the Earth event as a public relations opportunity. With dozens of journalists arriving at Sellafield for the Easter parade, we had a chance to gain valuable publicity for our side of the nuclear story. I decided to negotiate with Tom Burke, the Director of Friends of the Earth, and Walt Patterson, who led its anti-nuclear activities, to see if we could agree how their day of protest should be organized and managed.

Eventually we agreed that it was not in the interests of either Friends of the Earth or BNFL for there to be any violence. Both organizations wanted to come out of the event with their reputations for reasonableness intact. We also agreed that as Tony Benn wanted public debate, there should be public debate. Friends of the Earth has never been a militant environmental organization, in the way that the misleadingly named Greenpeace is. Their leaders coveted respectability for their views. Tom Burke and Walt Patterson believed that they could stop the reprocessing of overseas fuel, perhaps all reprocessing, by force of argument and assiduous political lobbying, rather than by blocking pipelines or invading industrial plants – and came close to doing so.

Some of the senior managers at Sellafield were astonished when I told them how far I had gone in committing BNFL to help organize the Friends of the Earth visit to the site. I had agreed that Sellafield would provide speakers to debate the merits of reprocessing with their representatives throughout the day. My reasoning was that if we refused to get involved in the event the demonstrators, finding themselves without anyone to argue with, would have time on their hands. They might then decide to try to draw attention to their cause in other, more mischievous ways.

I had therefore agreed with Friends of the Earth that the interminable debate planned for the day of protest would take place on land owned by BNFL near the main entrance to Sellafield. The road in between this spot and the site's perimeter fence would be no man's land, which Tom Burke agreed his members would be told not to cross. Anyone who did could be treated as a potential troublemaker and arrested, with the support of Friends of the Earth.

I asked the Sellafield management to provide a platform, microphones and loudspeakers for the debate and to tip off local agricultural show caterers to set up food and drink marquees, as I wanted to keep the demonstrators in well-fed good humour. We even provided portable lavatories and a crèche. As a final touch, I had a leaflet prepared explaining reprocessing. It took the stance that the demonstrators were clearly ill-informed and that we had a duty to put them straight with the facts. I arranged for the leaflet to be left on the train taking their supporters back to London, as I did not want to antagonize them while they were at Sellafield.

The day went off better than we could have hoped. Martyn Lewis, then the Northern Correspondent of Independent Television News, did a piece for the main ITN news bulletins that night in which he said that he was unsure whether he had been at a pro-nuclear or anti-nuclear rally. Friends of the

Earth muttered something about making the Easter demonstration at Sellafield an annual event, but they have not held one since. What Martyn Lewis and the demonstrators did not know was just how nervous the Sellafield management was that day. At my insistence the huge contingent of policemen brought in from all the other BNFL sites to assist the local force had been kept hidden at the back of the main administration building and the canteen. All the protesters and journalists saw was a handful of policemen on traffic and crowd marshalling duties.

At the time I thought that the security precautions insisted upon by Peter Mummery, who was then the site's General Manager, were over the top. Now, as a result of a serious security breach involving the environmental protesters from Greenpeace which occurred at Sellafield in 1995, I believe that Peter was right to be cautious.

Although its Easter 1976 demonstration was a bit of a damp squib, Friends of the Earth continued to lead the anti-Sellafield campaign for several more years after that. It was the main objector at the THORP public inquiry, pursuing most of the arguments against reprocessing advanced in the Flowers Report and a few more of its own besides. Despite the adversarial nature of the inquiry proceedings inside Whitehaven Civic Hall, relationships between BNFL staff and Friends of the Earth representatives outside the hall were entirely amicable. We joined together in five-a-side football matches, car rallies, quiz nights and other social events designed to while away the months in an isolated area which was new to many of us.

When the inquiry inspector came down firmly in favour of the THORP proposal and the plant won Government approval, it was as though Friends of the Earth's anti-nuclear campaigners lost heart. Many of their natural supporters began to look for something more telling than the reasoned arguments against nuclear power and reprocessing provided by Tom Burke and Walt Patterson. They were ready for action

– and Greenpeace stepped in and gave them what they wanted. Argument was quickly replaced by anger and aggression.

I first became aware of the lengths to which members of Greenpeace were prepared to go to gain publicity for their various causes towards the end of 1979, when the environmental organization announced that it intended to stop imports of spent nuclear fuel into Sellafield for reprocessing. Its first objective would be to prevent the next shipment of spent fuel from the Magnox stations in Japan being unloaded at Barrow-in-Furness, along the coast from Sellafield.

BNFL was preparing to expand the Barrow facility in preparation for the transport of oxide fuel from Japan for storage and subsequent reprocessing in THORP and this was an obvious trial of strength. The Japanese business eventually led to the creation of a fleet of six purpose-built ships, operated by Pacific Nuclear Transport Limited (PNTL), a BNFL associate company with minority Japanese and French shareholdings.

From the statements made by Greenpeace, it was obvious that their threat to disrupt the Japanese shipping business was real. In January 1980 BNFL persuaded the British Transport Docks Board (BTDB), which owned the Barrow docks, to take out an injunction against Greenpeace Limited and three of its UK Directors, David McTaggart, Alan Thornton and Peter Wilkinson (the main anti-nuclear spokesman), restraining them from interfering with the free navigation of vessels into and out of the docks.

Greenpeace was not to be deterred so easily. Two months after the injunction was granted, on 25 March, the *Pacific Fisher* was entering Barrow with its cargo of spent fuel when three inflatable dinghies were launched from a Greenpeace vessel, the *Rainbow Warrior.* The dinghies sped up the channel, overtaking the *Pacific Fisher.* They then zig-zagged across its bows, forcing the Trinity House pilot who was in charge of the vessel to slow down to what he regarded as a dangerously reduced speed, given the tidal conditions.

When the *Pacific Fisher* reached the harbour it had to enter a lock, where it was to tie up. With the inflatables still buzzing the ship, the pilot was unable to moor the *Pacific Fisher* port side on, as instructed by the harbour master, and tried to moor starboard side on, but that manoeuvre was blocked. The pilot was unable to moor alongside either wall of the lock and finally moored the *Pacific Fisher* with her starboard bow on the south wall and her port quarters on the north wall, at some risk of damaging the ship. More skirmishes took place when the vessel was inside the docks and an inflatable craft owned by Greenpeace was crushed. Fortunately no one was injured. The next day the people manning the remaining Greenpeace dinghies attempted to delay the unloading of the spent fuel, again at some risk to themselves and others.

Such a flagrant breach of the terms of the injunction could not be ignored. Although the British Transport Docks Board was initially reluctant to get involved, Peter Green, my deputy as Company Secretary at BNFL and the company's Chief Legal Adviser, persuaded it that it must bring proceedings against Greenpeace. The BTDB complained in the High Court that Greenpeace had disobeyed the injunction served on them only two months earlier and asked that the three defendants – the Greenpeace UK directors named in the original injunction – be sent to prison for contempt or that the British assets of Greenpeace be seized, or both.

At the High Court hearing before Mr Justice Pain the Greenpeace defendants admitted contempt of court – they could hardly do otherwise – but insisted that they did not intend any disrespect for the court. In his judgement, Mr Justice Pain said that it would be wrong to regard the proceedings as being in any sense an attempt to suppress the free expression of opinion. The proceedings were simply an attempt by a body which was charged with the operation of the docks to operate them efficiently and properly – and that alone was the matter with which the court was concerned. I agree with both of those sentiments. Greenpeace must never be allowed to place itself above the law, any more than BNFL should be allowed to do so – but nor must it be gagged.

Mr Justice Pain made another point during his judgement which I think people should bear in mind when they see television pictures of intrepid Greenpeace crew members in small inflatable boats bravely harassing larger vessels on the high seas, a tactic which Greenpeace continues to use despite the warning given to them in the High Court in 1980. In his evidence, Peter Wilkinson had said that he did not believe that complaints about the way the Greenpeace inflatables had buzzed around the *Pacific Fisher* like angry bees were justified. 'I do not accept that the presence of our tiny inflatable crafts could have had the slightest influence over the progress of this vessel and it was not my intention that they should have,' he said. One might well ask why the inflatables were there at all in that case. But quite apart from the fact that the progress of the *Pacific Fisher* clearly had been affected, the fallacy of that position, as Mr Justice Pain pointed out, is that it took no account of the humanity and concern of other, more reasonable, people.

For example, the Trinity House pilot, as a natural consequence of someone cutting across his bows, might be expected to reduce speed, whatever the tidal conditions. 'To put it in terms which may be more familiar to those on land, if you step off the pavement in front of a moving vehicle, it is a natural consequence of your act that the driver will try to avoid you, because he is an ordinary, humane person,' Mr Justice Pain said.

Despite the clear-cut nature of the offence, the Greenpeace defendants were dealt with rather kindly by the court. Greenpeace Limited was fined £500 and the three individuals £100 each for contempt of court, after giving undertakings that they would not repeat their actions. Costs were awarded to the British Transport Docks Board.

Greenpeace did not stop trying to prevent the use of Barrow docks by ships carrying spent nuclear fuel from overseas, however. It simply changed its strategy. In July 1981 it provided financial support to a supposedly independent anti-nuclear organization, the Barrow Action Group (BAG), which brought a High Court action against BNFL, Barrow Council and the BTDB, claiming that construction work carried out by BNFL on the expansion of Ramsden dock was illegal as no planning permission had been obtained for what was being described in the local press as 'a new atom terminal'.

In fact, BNFL had considered whether planning permission was needed for the development and, because of the anti-nuclear attitude of some of the Labour councillors on Barrow Council at that time, we were worried about our chances of getting it. But Peter Green came to the conclusion that the development was covered by a General Development Order which already applied to 'operational land' owned by the BTDB and he persuaded the Docks Board and the Town Clerk of Barrow that this was the case. It was this which BAG, supported by Greenpeace, decided to challenge.

BAG got as far as the High Court, but on legal advice dropped its action there, accepting that the General Development Order did indeed cover the construction of the new terminal at Ramsden dock as BNFL, the BTDB and the Town Clerk had said. At a public meeting called by BAG to explain what had gone wrong and to discuss how its costs were to be met, Peter Wilkinson said, 'I feel responsible because it was our digging around that led to the action', and there is no doubt that Greenpeace was the driving force behind the case.

BAG had collected £3,600 to cover the cost of its High Court action, made up of a donation of £1,000 from Greenpeace, £1,900 from a concert given by John Williams, the classical guitarist, and nearly £700 from a general appeal for funds in Barrow. After expenditure, the income netted down to around £1,700 – and BAG faced costs which it assessed at around £5,000. As BNFL estimated its own costs at between £3,000 and £4,000 and there were two other organizations involved, that was a low estimate.

Peter Wilkinson told the meeting that he believed BAG was in a strong position; both BNFL and Barrow Council were unlikely to take legal action over costs because of bad publicity. He was right. Without consulting BNFL or the Docks Board, Barrow Council announced that it would accept a nominal payment of £500 towards its costs. The BTDB said that it would follow BNFL's lead and, after a great deal of agonizing, the BNFL board took my advice and asked for only £600. The BTDB followed suit.

Peter Green thought I was wrong to let BAG off the hook and he was probably right. We did not get any thanks for the gesture and won no publicity prizes. I consoled myself with the thought that Greenpeace had now lost both of the actions which it had taken or inspired at Barrow and BNFL was free to expand its terminal. A few thousand pounds in unrecovered costs was a small price to pay for that. And the terminal still flourishes to this day. It has operated efficiently and well and there have been no accidents of note – certainly none of a significant radiological nature.

Greenpeace now turned its attention away from Barrow to Sellafield itself. In 1983 it started to monitor discharges of low-level radioactive effluent into the Irish Sea, sending samples off for analysis, with attendant publicity. It was during one of these exercises that Greenpeace divers alleged that they were seriously contaminated by the solvent slick which led to the November 1983 Beach Incident at Sellafield and to BNFL being prosecuted. Greenpeace immediately claimed that this event would never have become known to the public if its members had not measured the high radiation levels coming off the slick and I have already acknowledged that in my view this is at least partly true. I am convinced that if the slick had been dispersed in the sea as expected, Sellafield would have kept quiet about it.

Building on this publicity triumph, Greenpeace announced that it intended to block the pipeline, which takes low-level liquid waste out to sea from the Sellafield site through a pipe one and a half miles long. I told the BNFL board that as the site's operation would be jeopardized if this happened, we had no option but to seek a further injunction in the High Court, this one aimed at stopping Greenpeace from attacking the pipeline.

My attitude towards Greenpeace was summarized in the words I prepared for the press statement issued when BNFL was granted a temporary injunction by Mr Justice Taylor on 22 November 1983. As the solvent slick had led to the use of local beaches being restricted for several weeks by then, this was not the most auspicious time to go to law against a popular environmental organization running complementary campaigns designed to save the whale and to stop the culling of baby seals and other cuddly animals. I was therefore careful to emphasize that the injunction we had obtained was designed solely to prevent Greenpeace blocking the pipeline, not taking samples.

I also said that BNFL regarded Greenpeace's threat as highly irresponsible and potentially dangerous. Nevertheless, I acknowledged that they had an inalienable right to question our activities at Sellafield and to try to influence public opinion and Government policy by reasoned arguments and protest events staged within the law. But Greenpeace had no right to take the law into its own hands by taking direct, physical action to interfere with BNFL's lawful business.

In that press release I also pointed out that Sellafield operated under the terms of a site licence issued by the Nuclear Installations Inspectors of the Health and Safety Executive and in accordance with authorizations for the disposal of radioactive waste issued by the Department of the Environment and the Ministry of Agriculture, Fisheries and Food. Implicit in my statement was the belief that most members of the public would accept that responsible Government regulation should be good enough for Greenpeace and for anyone else. The fact is, however, that the public was becoming increasingly dissatisfied with the regulatory process. By maintaining a high profile for its direct action while attacking the adequacy of Government controls, Greenpeace came to be regarded as the true regulator of Sellafield by many people, even in Cumbria.

Part of the problem I believe, is that the Government and organizations such as the National Radiological Protection Board do not do enough to justify the health and safety standards they set. Far too often BNFL and other companies conducting industrial activities opposed by Greenpeace are left to defend these standards themselves. To which the easy and obvious response is 'Well, they would say that, wouldn't they?'

When BNFL was granted the temporary injunction by Mr Justice Taylor restraining Greenpeace Limited, Greenpeace (Rainbow Warrior Holdings), Greenpeace UK Limited, Greenpeace Environmental Trust and Peter Wilkinson from damaging, blocking or interfering with the Sellafield sea discharge pipeline, Greenpeace chose to ignore it. For two days, on 23 and 24 November 1983, a Greenpeace team did their level best to block the pipelines. They were unsuccessful, but once again their deliberate breach of the injunction could not be ignored. It was back to the High Court. On 1 December we started sequestration proceedings before Mr Justice Comyn. Three times during the hearing the judge asked Greenpeace to consider giving him an assurance that they would not again attempt to interfere with the pipeline. He adjourned the hearing on each occasion, but every time – once after consulting their members who were still stationed off the pipeline on the Greenpeace ship the *Cedarlea* – Greenpeace came back into court and refused to give the undertaking.

Mr Justice Comyn appeared to have some sympathy for Greenpeace's objectives – indeed, Greenpeace's counsel jokingly suggested at one stage that he should apply for membership of the environmental group – but he also understood his duty as a judge to see court orders observed. This is reflected in what he had to say when he passed judgement: 'It is tragic how many people feel they can either with an air of martyrdom or defiance take on the might of the law. The law is here to protect us in every facet of human life. It is at our beck and call, both criminal and civil, if we or our families or our work are in danger. We cannot have it both ways – we cannot obey only those laws we think should be obeyed. It is all or nothing. Anyone who takes on the law deliberately comes off worse. Let that be widely known.'

Mr Justice Comyn said that the Greenpeace defendants were seriously in contempt of court and that he had considered sequestration, the freezing of all their assets – 'thus literally shutting them down and shutting them up'. However, acknowledging that they held views which they were entitled to hold and free, peacefully and lawfully, to propagate and to work for, he had decided not to order sequestration 'on this occasion'.

Instead, he imposed a fine totalling £50,000, spread over Greenpeace Limited, Greenpeace (Rainbow Warrior Holdings) and Greenpeace Environmental Trust (Greenpeace UK Limited apparently had no assets). The three companies were also ordered to pay the costs of the proceedings on the highest possible basis. The total sums had to be paid by 1 February 1984, the Judge said.

Before that date, on 12 January, BNFL went back to the High Court seeking to have the temporary injunction made permanent. The Greenpeace defendants opposed this, arguing that BNFL had suffered no permanent damage as a result of their actions and that because of the Beach Incident BNFL itself did not come to the court with clean hands, as it was in breach of the Radioactive Substances Act 1960 and of the recently introduced regulatory principle that it must keep radioactive discharges 'as low as reasonably achievable'.

His Honour Judge Smout dismissed this defence, taking the view that the court was not the place to test the ALARA principle. If it was a matter of public concern, it might call for a public inquiry, he said. Or if there was evidence of a breach of the law by BNFL, as the defendants said, there might be a prosecution or other civil proceedings. But this was no defence in the action before him.

Judge Smout therefore granted BNFL a permanent injunction restraining Greenpeace and its agents from damaging, blocking, physically obstructing or interfering with the pipeline. Judgement was given for damages and interest, to be assessed at a later date. Once again costs were awarded to BNFL.

On the same day, Greenpeace applied to Mr Justice Comyn, who had imposed the £50,000 fine for contempt of court a month earlier, for an extension of time to pay the fine. Greenpeace explained that it had so far received only £36,000 from public subscriptions. The judge ordered payment into court of the £36,000 which had been collected, remitting the balance of the fine. This effectively put an end to the action, except for BNFL's assessment and collection of damages and costs. In fact we decided to be magnanimous again, having obtained the perpetual injunction we sought. As long as Greenpeace did not appeal against the permanent injunction by 27 February 1984, the last date on which it could appeal, we would waive our costs and the damages awarded to us. They did not appeal and we did not pursue our claim against them.

In July of the following year BNFL was convicted at Carlisle Crown Court on charges relating to the Beach Incident and four months after that Greenpeace – just as litigious as BNFL – went back to court. Although it was now nineteen months after the date by which it should have lodged any appeal, it sought – and was granted – an extension of time to appeal against the permanent injunction not to attack the pipeline. I was furious, partly with myself for persuading the BNFL board to waive our claim for costs, which were of the order of £40,000. So much for magnanimity. We appealed against the extension of time granted to Greenpeace and won. We were also awarded our costs – and this time we collected. The permanent injunction prohibiting attacks on the pipeline remained in place.

Around this period Greenpeace changed their director responsible for nuclear campaign activities. Peter Wilkinson moved on, to be succeeded by George Pritchard. The new man seemed to me to be more in the Friends of the Earth mould, someone who wanted to understand the nuclear power industry, not just oppose it blindly because that was the position of Greenpeace internationally, dictated from on high within that somewhat autocratic organization. George Pritchard commissioned much of the original research work which led to Yorkshire Television's influential programme on childhood leukaemias, which did more damage to Sellafield's public image than any amount of frenetic activity in small inflatables.

George was also prepared to discuss his reasons for opposing nuclear power with us and was clearly impressed when Christopher Harding tried to open up a dialogue with environmentalists. One of my initiatives in the aftermath of the 1983 Beach Incident was to encourage the trade unions within BNFL to set up their own organization to counter the anti-nuclear lobbying by Arthur Scargill and other trade union leaders, particularly those who led the National Union of Seamen, which went on at the Trades Union Congress (TUC) and Labour Party conferences. It was at my instigation and with my covert support that the National Council for the Nuclear Industry (NCNI) was set up and it was with the help of my political liaison staff that the NCNI developed into the highly effective lobby organization it has become.

At one of the political party conferences a group of BNFL employees, there under the banner of the NCNI, sought out George Pritchard and invited him to visit the company's factories, including Sellafield. Somewhat to their surprise, he accepted, on condition that the visit was kept secret from the media. When they heard what had happened, some of the Sellafield managers complained to me that the workers had no right to issue invitations to the site – that was the prerogative of the head of the site.

I told them not to be so pompous and that I supported the NCNI, which should be congratulated not criticized. If we believed in what we were doing, we should not be afraid of anyone gaining a better understanding of our operations. The invitation stood and I promised George Pritchard that his request for privacy would be respected. In November 1986, after visiting the other factories, George Pritchard went up to Sellafield, the main interest – and target – of Greenpeace. He was clearly impressed by what he saw.

On the final night of his tour George went to the Wasdale Head Inn at the end of Wastwater, that starkly beautiful lake near Sellafield, for the annual 'world's biggest liar' competition held there. This involves people inventing and telling tall stories and there have been several winners from Sellafield, much to the amusement of the local media. A BBC Radio Cumbria reporter was covering the event the night George Pritchard turned up and Jake Kelly, Head of Media Relations at Sellafield, pointed him out, suggesting to the reporter that he might get an interesting interview if he asked the Director of Greenpeace UK what he was doing in the Sellafield area. Given our agreement that Mr Pritchard's visit would be kept secret, Jake was rather mischievous, perhaps, but George did not have to give the radio reporter an interview, he chose to do so.

During the interview George admitted that he had been round Sellafield and confessed that his visit had changed his views about the place. 'As a man who has seen a fair amount of industry, the standards of cleanliness and maintenance on the site are the best I have ever seen,' George said. He also praised BNFL's willingness to talk to environmentalists and said that he wished other industrialists would take the same attitude as Christopher Harding, who had committed himself to ending secrecy in the nuclear industry.

Mr Pritchard also praised BNFL for allowing him to go

anywhere he wanted at Sellafield. As well as visiting the £400 million fuel-handling plant and the £126 million SIXEP, which had only just been opened by Margaret Thatcher, he had visited the plutonium line and some of the older plants on the site. 'This has given me the opportunity to judge what it was like in the past, what the company is doing about it, and what it will be like in the future,' George Pritchard said. 'There are still things within that old plant we would like changed and we will produce a report at the end of this on the whole of the nuclear fuel cycle. As a result of this, hopefully, the management and workers will try to get those things done. Now, if it is possible for them to do those things, then maybe there is a future for this industry.' Mr Pritchard's words are taken directly from a transcript of his BBC radio interview.

That local radio interview was picked up immediately by the national BBC network and then by other sections of the media and created a minor sensation. It also got George Pritchard into trouble with the international Greenpeace organization and four days after giving the interview he retracted his statement, claiming that his comments had been taken out of context and distorted. This time, in an interview with Border Television up in Cumbria, Mr Pritchard said that Greenpeace had not changed its views about Sellafield.

'Unfortunately, I did a radio interview,' George Pritchard said. 'It was an interview of about six minutes which was cut by Radio Four to about fifty seconds, which distorted the whole interview.' Mr Pritchard went on to say that his impression was that BNFL had put an awful lot of money into cleaning up the Sellafield site. 'Unfortunately, as long as that industry has to produce waste in liquid form for ten years before being vitrified, then I can never give the go-ahead for the industry. There is a future for Sellafield, but the future is in closing the industry down. It will need skills and workers – that is the future we see for Sellafield.'

These attempts to correct his original statement did not cut much ice with the media or, it would seem, with the leaders of Greenpeace. Three months later, in March 1987, George Pritchard resigned, to be succeeded by Lord Melchett, who quickly made it clear that he wanted no part in a constructive dialogue with Christopher Harding or anyone else at BNFL.

Greenpeace quickly returned to its old ways. Notwithstanding the permanent injunction restraining several Greenpeace companies from attacking the Sellafield sea discharge pipeline, we learned that a fresh attempt was to be made to block the line, this time by different Greenpeace companies. I learned a lot about Greenpeace's tactics and structure during this exercise.

Although it makes great play of the secretiveness of BNFL and other organizations it campaigns against, demanding that they become more publicly accountable, Greenpeace is itself a highly complex, secretive organization, seemingly accountable to no one other than its international leaders. It employs various nationals and registers its ships and companies in several parts of the world, making it extremely difficult for company lawyers to ring it around with injunctions in Britain or any other country where it operates or to seek retribution for the damage it causes.

Greenpeace thrives on publicity, and diligent monitoring of the media coverage of the antics taking place off the Sellafield pipeline, together with careful detective work by Peter Green and his Legal Directorate team, led us to the leaders of the latest Greenpeace attack. Just after midnight on 1 June 1987 – a bare three months after George Pritchard's resignation – we obtained an *ex parte* injunction from a duty judge against the Greenpeace companies we understood to be involved. Injunctions were also granted against Hans Guyt, who was being described by the media as the Greenpeace expedition leader, and Walter Beckman, the captain of the Dutch Greenpeace vessel the *Sirius*. Peter Green arranged for copies of the injunctions to be taken out to the Greenpeace vessel and handed over to the crew – real cloak and dagger stuff.

The *Sirius* was the mother ship for the inflatable boats

which were once again being used to get Greenpeace divers to the end of the pipeline. None of these people were British nationals and just to complicate matters further, although the Greenpeace Council, the organization's international controlling body, operated from Lewes in Sussex at that time, it was registered in Holland.

For two days we were uncertain whether anything was going to happen. Perhaps the new injunction would be obeyed. Nevertheless, I was getting anxious as divers employed at Sellafield swam in the Irish Sea off the end of the pipeline alongside the Greenpeace divers, circling each other menacingly at times. The reports I received from Sellafield made what was going on sound like something out of a James Bond film and I became genuinely concerned that the situation was getting out of hand. There was undoubtedly a great deal of ill-feeling and tempers became more and more frayed, particularly when an Irish girl who was a member of the Greenpeace diving team spat in the face of one of the Sellafield divers and called him foul names.

We tried to get help from the police, Government departments or anyone else we could think of who might have an interest in seeing the law upheld, but without success. The problem is that the law relating to attacks on off-shore property is vague and ambiguous. I tried to interest the Department of Energy's lawyers and civil servants in getting the law clarified or replaced, but they had done nothing about it by the time I left BNFL. The legal uncertainty emerged when I tried to stop the Greenpeace attack on the pipeline before it happened, pointing to the threats coming from the crew of the *Sirius*.

First of all the Sellafield management asked the UKAEA constabulary, which polices the site and which is paid for this service by BNFL, to stop Greenpeace. They declined to do anything, arguing that they had no powers of arrest at sea. Sellafield then approached the Cumbria constabulary, but that force also cited uncertainty over its legal powers as a reason for not taking any action – plus the fact that it had no boats!

We even made an informal approach to the Royal Navy and the coastguard for help, but were told it was not their responsibility either.

Because the Sellafield management was unwilling to risk its relationship with the Cumbria police, which has always been a good one, the site asked me to play the heavy and apply whatever pressure I could as Company Secretary of BNFL. I had several conversations with Chief Inspector Joe Ullock, of the Cumbria force, and tried to persuade him to do something. I know from conversations we had later, in less stressful times, that he found my persistence irritating. In the absence of legal clarity, no one wanted to get involved in a situation which was becoming increasingly political. BNFL, having effectively closed local beaches, was firmly cast as the villain of the piece and Greenpeace as the great defender of the environment. All we could do was sit back and wait for something to happen.

On 3 June 1987 Greenpeace finally breached the Sellafield discharge pipeline – four years after its first attempt. The event was well publicized, which was what Greenpeace wanted, but it did not take long for BNFL to reopen the pipeline and continue reprocessing. Peter Green and his team obtained a court order freezing some of Greenpeace's assets, including the *Sirius* and the bank accounts of Greenpeace Holland and Greenpeace International. The bank accounts were subsequently released when Greenpeace gave a guarantee of £200,000 if BNFL won the action.

It took no fewer than twenty-seven court actions in England and Holland to get to this position, showing the complexity of the Greenpeace organization and international law. In October Hans Guyt and Walter Beckman were imprisoned for three months for contempt of court. BNFL finally brought the pipeline saga to an end in May 1988 when the company agreed to a Greenpeace request for BNFL to discontinue proceedings against various parts of its organization for the damage to the pipeline. Three Greenpeace bodies – its

International Council, Dutch Greenpeace and the owners of the *Sirius* – each volunteered to accept a permanent injunction from the High Court preventing them from attempting to interfere with the pipeline, or assisting others to do so. In addition, a payment of £80,000 was made to BNFL for damages and legal costs.

Two years later and it was back to the high seas when a vessel identified as the *MV Greenpeace* intercepted the *Pacific Sandpiper*, a ship owned by Pacific Nuclear Transport Limited, which was carrying spent fuel from Japan towards Barrow-in-Furness, after having unloaded part of its cargo at Cherbourg for reprocessing at the French reprocessing plant at Cap La Hague.

The *Pacific Sandpiper* was moving at about ten knots when the *MV Greenpeace* launched several inflatable craft and a helicopter took off from her deck. The inflatables wove around the *Pacific Sandpiper* and the helicopter hovered at the same height as the *Pacific Sandpiper*'s wheelhouse, about fifty yards ahead of the moving ship. The *MV Greenpeace* then proceeded to steer a course across the bows of the *Pacific Sandpiper*, suddenly changing direction and moving across the bows the opposite way, forcing the *Pacific Sandpiper* to take evasive action.

Then it was back to the Bond film scenario – *Plutoniumfinger* perhaps. After thirty minutes of fencing, the inflatables came alongside the *Pacific Sandpiper*. With the aid of rope ladders, six Greenpeace protesters clambered on board the ship, spreading themselves out over the deck and chaining themselves to various parts of the superstructure. The protesters refused to move and demanded that the ship return to Japan.

On paper, the Greenpeace boarding operation sounds relatively easy. In fact it was extremely hazardous. All this happened on the high seas and I was later shown film taken from the *Pacific Sandpiper* which shows members of the crew hosing down the Greenpeace raiders and pushing their boats away from the side of the ship with long poles. Feelings ran high among crew members anxious to get home after several weeks at sea.

From what I saw on the film I felt there was a risk that somebody could have been killed and I formally requested Alan Salmon, BNFL's Transport Director, who was responsible for the PNTL operation, to ensure that nothing like what I had seen would happen again. I told him that I could understand the frustration of the *Pacific Sandpiper's* crew, but it was essential that the crews of the PNTL nuclear fuel carriers did nothing to endanger the lives of the Greenpeace members in their small dinghies, however much they were provoked. Alan promised that there would be no repeat action; but I have a feeling that his sympathies lay with the crew of the *Pacific Sandpiper.* I had some sympathy for the crew too. The behaviour of the Greenpeace team was outrageous.

Because six protesters were still chained to the superstructure, the *Pacific Sandpiper* put in at Milford Haven in South Wales, instead of heading up to Barrow-in-Furness. On arrival there on 28 August 1990, the local police removed the protesters from the ship and she was able to continue her voyage to Barrow. I wondered whether the Milford Haven police were aware of the uncertainty over powers of arrest at sea which had prevented the Cumbria force from acting three years earlier, but we were glad of their intervention at the time. Two days later, shutting the stable door after the horse had bolted to some extent, BNFL was granted an *ex parte* injunction in the High Court relating to actions of the kind carried out from the *MV Greenpeace* and three months after that Greenpeace gave undertakings to obey the terms of the injunction. BNFL was awarded costs again – and collected.

I was reminded of this high seas adventure again in June 1995, when Greenpeace succeeded in preventing the deep sea disposal of the *Brent Spar*, a redundant 65,000-tonne loading buoy owned by Shell, forcing the company into an amazing volte-face in the process. Shell handled the public relations of this event badly, beginning at the start of the escapade as a

Greenpeace helicopter attempted to lower activists on to the deck of the floating oil tank. As the helicopter hovered over the *Brent Spar* high-pressure hoses were turned on to it from vessels owned by Shell, threatening to force it out of the skies.

As I watched the television news pictures of the Greenpeace helicopter apparently dancing on the end of the water jets I could not believe what I was seeing. It was obvious to me that by appearing to place the lives of the people in the helicopter in jeopardy, no matter how slight, Shell would now be branded the irresponsible party in this action, losing any chance it had of gaining or retaining public support. Those pictures, as much as anything else, had an influence on what was to follow, despite Shell's public statements that it was determined to stick to its guns and the pledge of full support which the company received in the House of Commons from John Major on Monday 20 June.

Given the number of times successive Governments had withdrawn their support from the nuclear industry as soon as its plans for disposing of radioactive waste came under attack from environmental organizations, I could only envy Shell. I wondered how its political lobbyists had managed to persuade the Government to be so resolute, particularly as other European governments were issuing statements opposing the dumping of the *Brent Spar* 150 miles out in the Atlantic, north-west of the Hebrides, at a depth of around 7,800 metres. I assumed that the next step would be for Shell to seek High Court injunctions restraining Greenpeace, if that was possible in maritime law.

The very next day, to the astonishment of everyone, even the environmental protesters, Shell capitulated. It announced that it would do what Greenpeace wanted and decommission the *Brent Spar* on land. Greenpeace was jubilant. The Government was rightly furious.

The reason Shell gave publicly for its about-turn was that it had changed its mind because of the level of opposition it had encountered from several European governments. But that opposition, fostered by Greenpeace, must surely have been expected. Shell also lost substantial business at the petrol pumps, mainly in Germany, where Greenpeace demonstrators picketed petrol stations. That must have been a factor too. But I have also heard it said that Shell backed off in face of the terrorist-like activities of a group of people who blew up one Shell petrol station in Germany and tried to blow up another.

If that is so, I am concerned on two counts. First, although that action was rightly condemned by Greenpeace itself, which dissociated itself from the activities of this bunch of environmental zealots, it does point up the danger of violent activists latching on to Greenpeace campaigns – always a concern at Sellafield. Secondly, if my information is correct, I would be as concerned about major companies giving way to terrorist action or threats as I would be if governments did so.

If Shell had gone ahead with the decommissioning of the *Brent Spar* on land, it would have set a precedent which the oil industry would have come to regret. If dumping the *Brent Spar* at sea was the best practical environmental option, as Shell and the Government insisted, then that was the option which should have been exercised. Giving way in face of a Greenpeace campaign which even some environmentalists believe to have been ill-judged will simply encourage further opposition to the dumping of any redundant oil rig facilities in the deep sea, whatever they contain in the way of toxic materials.

In the event, Shell appeared to have been saved from making this blunder when Greenpeace was forced to admit that it had grossly overestimated the quantity of toxic materials on board the *Brent Spar*. Shell then announced that it was reconsidering its decision to decommission on land and the *Brent Spar* may yet be sunk – as oil industry disposal policy once looked in danger of being.

The last Greenpeace campaign with which I was involved while employed at BNFL came during the months leading up to the planned start-up of reprocessing in THORP. It began with Greenpeace obtaining tens of thousands of signatures from all over the country for a petition urging the Government to refuse permission for the plant to be commissioned. Despite opposition from my new Chairman, John Guinness, who thought that politicians and civil servants were far too sophisticated to be impressed by such an obvious device, I felt BNFL had to respond. I therefore encouraged the National Council for the Nuclear Industry to organize a counter-petition, demanding immediate Government approval for the start-up.

Cumbrians Opposed to a Radioactive Environment (CORE), another apparently independent organization with strong links to Greenpeace, then asked Sellafield's permission to stage a small protest against THORP outside the site's main gate. Without seeking my views, Sellafield agreed, even though I was BNFL's THORP campaign director when allowed to be by the Chairman. The first thing I knew about what was going on was when I read in the newspaper that Greenpeace proper had taken over the protest event, which would now feature the Irish pop group U2.

I immediately issued a statement that this event, which might well have attracted tens of thousands of people – whether they were anti-nuclear or not – would not take place on BNFL land. We were simply not prepared for such an invasion. When Greenpeace continued to insist that the free concert would go ahead, we obtained an injunction prohibiting the use of BNFL land. There were many disappointed young people around in west Cumbria, which is not well served by the entertainment industry. They included some of the Sellafield apprentices, who were apparently all set to turn up at the concert dedicated to destroying their jobs. Although the U2 members went up to Cumbria on the designated day and gained some publicity – for the group and for Greenpeace – there was no free concert outside Sellafield's main gates.

For fifteen years while I was with BNFL the company

had to fend off determined attempts by Greenpeace to stop reprocessing, but none of them was as significant and potentially dangerous as what happened when around 200 Greenpeace members invaded the Sellafield site over the Easter weekend of 1995, after I had left the company. They did so in order to highlight what they claimed were the links between civil nuclear power and the production of atomic weapons, on a day when nuclear non-proliferation talks began in New York between the UK, France, China, Russia and the US.

The raid on Sellafield coincided with a parallel Greenpeace protest at the Atomic Weapons Establishment site at Aldermaston, where a group of Greenpeace members sealed a pipe carrying mildly radioactive waste water into the River Thames. Some of the sting was taken out of the Aldermaston demonstration in the following day's newspapers, however, when Douglas Hurd, the then Foreign Secretary, was reported as saying at the non-proliferation talks that the UK was to cease production of plutonium and enriched uranium for use in nuclear weapons. I am not sure whether he was reported correctly or not, but the statement is incorrect in any event.

Greenpeace's invasion of Sellafield had many worrying aspects. The dawn raid appeared to take the UKAEA constabulary and the Cumbria police completely by surprise, although I know that they can usually rely on a tip-off from informants when events like this are planned. Campaigners wearing orange boiler suits or dressed as drums of plutonium – hardly inconspicuous apparel – swarmed over and through the security fence near the site's main gate and even over the gate itself.

Teams of Greenpeace supporters who had been given special targets were then able to achieve their objective of reaching THORP and the MOX plant, which was under construction for the production of mixed uranium and plutonium oxide fuel. Significantly, one of the teams knew how to get to the plutonium store and sprayed the word 'bollocks' on one of the walls to show that they had arrived there. That has to be a matter of concern, despite BNFL's attempt to play down the seriousness of what occurred. Frankly, I found one of the statements made by the company about the event alarming in its complacency. I would certainly not have allowed it to be issued if I had still been responsible for public information and security.

Discussing the security breach, BNFL had this to say:

> In common with other nuclear facilities, Sellafield deploys defence in depth to protect sensitive locations and processes. The prime purpose of the outer site fence is to demark the site boundary and is not intended to contribute significantly to the security of the site. Access was not gained to operational facilities and there was no danger to the facilities, employees or the public. Normal operations were maintained at all times.

I regard that statement as asinine and, if it was meant to reassure people, totally counter-productive. Let us examine it. Are we really meant to accept that a double fence, topped with barbed wire and patrolled by armed policemen and guard dogs twenty-four hours a day, has no real purpose other than to show where the site boundary is? And how can it be said that there was no danger to the plants when a couple of hundred demonstrators, who might have been armed terrorists for all BNFL knew when they poured on to the site unimpeded, reached the plutonium store, THORP and the MOX plant. Two of these facilities contain plutonium in various forms and the third is intended to do so when it is built. As far as the 'defence in depth' security principle is concerned, it seems to me that if determined terrorist invaders had reached the outside walls of the plutonium store, instead of the Greenpeace team, the only 'depth' left in the system would have been the use of weapons by those paid to protect the place.

If I had still been responsible to the BNFL board for security I would have ordered an immediate review of security at

Sellafield and announced publicly that the company took this security breach extremely seriously and intended to do everything possible to prevent a recurrence. From some of my former colleagues, I know that Roger Howsley, who had company-wide responsibility for security, and who used to report to me, was deeply perturbed by what happened and instituted an immediate review. BNFL should have said so at the time.

The local newspaper, the *Whitehaven News*, was right to draw attention to the real message to come out of this dangerous and irresponsible stunt by Greenpeace, its identification of faults in the security system at Sellafield. In a leader article, the paper had this to say:

> If it is that easy to get close to THORP and surrounding plant, then had the infiltration been of truly evil intent they could have blown the place heavens high, despite its massively strong construction and coded security systems. The consequences of that would have been horrendous.
>
> Security at the level we perceive it seems to leave something to be desired. Perhaps there is an additional something which would quickly have been in evidence if those who broke into Sellafield on Monday had not been there merely to protest. There might have been guns and there would certainly have been more animated action from the police than was apparent this week.
>
> We are aware of the procedures which guard each of the units inside the complex and the mightily strong nature of their construction. Nevertheless, it is better to stop infiltrators getting that far. We remain surprised Greenpeace got in so easily; amazed at how quickly they made uninterrupted progress from the perimeter to the working stations.
>
> To live as close to Sellafield as most of our readers do is to make a nodding acquiescence towards the safety of the plant and to hope that all is being done, all the time, to protect us. We are disturbed it was so easy for a couple of

> hundred people, hardly saboteurs and commando-trained, to gain entry to a nuclear reprocessing plant. It does not make us sleep easier at night.

I fully subscribe to those sentiments. I also believe that in drawing attention to serious security lapses at Sellafield, Greenpeace may be said to have been performing a public service. Nevertheless, I deplore the means by which they chose to do this. There can be no doubt that there was the potential for some of the Greenpeace marauders to get themselves killed during this operation, either as they scrambled over gates, fences and buildings in the half-light of dawn or because their intrusion on to the site was seen as a real threat by the armed policemen guarding some of Sellafield's most sensitive buildings and nuclear materials.

With its successful invasion of Sellafield, Greenpeace gained considerable publicity for its new anti-nuclear campaign, one which attempts to establish a link between civil nuclear power and the atomic weapons programme where none, in truth, exists. It will be encouraged by that and will not let go of the issue. I was disappointed by BNFL's initial, low-key public relations approach to that campaign, a bland attempt to reassure which would convince no one and which does not seem to have been thought through. In my view the company must rethink its public relations strategy for responding to such events, as well as its security arrangements. It took me a long time to get BNFL off the defensive and I would hate to see the company go back into its shell now, doing little more than respond to a succession of media stunts organized by Greenpeace.

Chapter Seven

Public Information:

Open and Honest

By now it must be apparent that for much of my career with BNFL, Sellafield was placed under virtual siege by the media, environmentalists and politicians, and the company's public information programme reflected this for at least a decade. With so much going wrong with the site's older plants and the newer ones still to be completed, BNFL was kept on the defensive until the mid-1980s. We could do little more than fight the fires of outraged public opinion as best we could as one accident followed another and a succession of new claims was made about the dangers of reprocessing. It took the 1983 Beach Incident at Sellafield and the infinitely more serious disaster at Chernobyl in the Ukraine in 1986 to bring about a change of attitude, forcing the company to get off the back foot and argue its case positively.

I was the architect of the 'open and honest' approach towards public information which was introduced by BNFL at a time of crisis for Sellafield and for the world-wide nuclear industry. I forced this change of policy through in face of opposition from the Government, from some of my fellow directors and from the management and trade unions at Sellafield itself. It was made clear to me that my job was on the line if it failed.

After the excitement of winning a famous victory over the anti-nuclear groups at the THORP public inquiry, the BNFL board thought it had the public relations game won. The natural instinct of people brought up to build and operate nuclear plants while sheltering under the umbrella protection of the Official Secrets Act was to step back into the Act's protective shade as quickly as possible. I had spent just over three years with 'hands on' responsibility for public information when the company decided that it was safe for me to move on to what it regarded as bigger and better things as Company Secretary and Director of Corporate Affairs. I retained overall responsibility for public information, however.

During my three years as Director of Information, I managed to persuade the BNFL board that the company needed a visitors' centre at Sellafield, somewhere that members of the public could go for information, entertainment or just to get out of the Lake District rain. I had ambitious plans for the centre, which I believed had tremendous possibilities if it was marketed properly, despite the remoteness of Sellafield. Nobody in authority at the site shared my vision, however, and unfortunately it was decided that the centre should be paid for by the company's reprocessing division, which was responsible for the operation of Sellafield, and placed under the site's control, not mine. It was a wrong decision, which I should have fought.

Gordon Williams, who was both publicity manager and my deputy at the time, did his best with the limited resources made available by people who were not really sold on the idea, but we ended up with a small, static exhibition on the upper floor of a two-storey building. There were as many working models as we could afford on a low budget, but for the most part the exhibition consisted of lots of words on panels which visitors were expected to read. The centre was tucked away near the apprentice training building, off the operating site, and it was poorly signposted. Underneath the exhibition floor was a dentist's surgery, with a bigger sign than that of the exhibition centre. It did not provide the warmest of welcomes to Sellafield.

On the formation of the company, public relations had been seen as part of BNFL's commercial effort, not as a vehicle for winning wider public acceptance. Gordon Williams, who had considerable flair for such things, was in charge of exhibitions, film-making, conferences and advertising. All of these activities were firmly oriented towards sales. I had to build up a press office and political lobbying capability quickly, in face of the acute public interest sparked off by the *Mirror*'s 'nuclear dustbin' campaign and Tony Benn's insistence on public debate. I put that responsibility on Brian Potts, who had started his career in nuclear power as a scientist at Sellafield and knew the site well. Brian also knew who we could trust to provide accurate information about what went on there in an emergency.

At the end of the THORP inquiry, which he covered for the BBC as its Cumbria Correspondent, I recruited Jake Kelly into a new post as head of Media Relations at Sellafield. This placed him firmly at the centre of the action. I insisted that Jake reported to me because I did not want him to be absorbed into Sellafield's secret society culture. Unfortunately, because of the suspicion which exists between the Sellafield management and anyone tied in to BNFL's headquarters operation at Risley, Jake was often caught up in the maelstrom of internal politics.

Occasionally, because he was seen by some of his colleagues at Sellafield as the Risley spy – an expression which I heard used many times – Jake was deprived of information which was essential to his job, placing him in extremely embarrassing situations at times. He nevertheless became a very accomplished spokesman for the company in Cumbria. He was the human face of Sellafield, a valuable member of the public relations team and an exceptional radio and television spokesman for the company.

This was the embryo public relations organization which was in place when I moved on to become Company Secretary and Director of Corporate Affairs. There was still a great deal for someone to do, particularly on the media and political liaison front, and BNFL decided to recruit my successor from outside the company. It was looking for someone with my sort of background in journalism and I was made responsible for finding my own replacement as Director of Information. To my considerable relief and pleasure Jeffrey Preece, a former colleague of mine from my early days with the *Birmingham Post*, volunteered himself when he heard about the job on the grapevine.

Jeff was already in his fifties when he joined BNFL, ten years older than me, and some thought I was wrong to bring in an older man. But I knew him to be a first-class communications practitioner, keen to take on a new challenge. I jumped at the chance of having such an experienced man working with me. Jeff had wide-ranging journalistic experience. He had started off on weekly newspapers with the *Sutton Coldfield News* before becoming Industrial Correspondent of the *Post* and then Midlands Correspondent of *The Times*. Later he became a radio and television reporter with the BBC. Jeff also had the advantage of public relations experience. He was head of information with the CEGB's West Midlands Region at the time he joined me and knew a great deal about the electricity supply industry which BNFL served.

For the first five years of his career with BNFL, Jeff Preece was almost totally engrossed in defending the company against attack, as I had been before him. We both felt frustrated about this. We knew that we could not go on allowing Greenpeace to set the public information agenda, but neither of us was certain how to go about turning the tables on them. Matters were brought to a head when the radioactive slick released from Sellafield led to a Government warning to people not to make unnecessary use of local beaches in late 1983 – a warning that stayed in force until the middle of 1984. We decided that we must go outside for help and carry out a full review of our public relations strategy.

In part, this review was also a response to the failure of an advertising campaign which I authorized in too much of a panic, without proper research into its likely effect. We tried to counter the public's indignation about the closure of the beaches by showing them how much BNFL had spent on reducing routine discharges of radioactive materials into the sea and how small these discharges now were, by comparison with what they had been at their peak. We did so by showing a very small box, the current discharges, set inside a very much larger box, the earlier discharges, with a suitable explanatory caption designed to show what a splendid job the company had done, with no expense spared.

Unfortunately, the research we carried out showed that the public had taken entirely the wrong messages from the ads. Instead of being impressed by the reductions BNFL had achieved, they questioned why there were any discharges to the Irish Sea at all. They also came to the conclusion that the peak discharges must have been extremely dangerous for BNFL to spend so much money on reducing them. I vowed that I would never again be hurried into advertising or any other publicity venture involving expenditure which was under my control; there must always be proper research first.

I discussed my feeling that we needed a total review of our public relations effort with Geoffrey Tucker, whom I had just appointed as the company's first external consultant, and who became part of the review team. Later I was to appoint Sir Bernard Ingham as a consultant as soon as he left Downing Street. I also obtained the consultancy services of Ken Woolmer, a former Labour MP, and Lord Basnett, a former General Secretary of the General and Municipal Workers Union, the trade union with the largest membership in BNFL, in order to balance the political representation.

The 'open and honest' policy towards public information which emerged from that review was formulated by me while Con Allday was still Chairman of BNFL, although his successor, Christopher Harding, is generally given credit for it. Where Christopher does deserve credit is for taking this policy, developing it and making himself the main focus for its expression. In that he was superb, fully deserving the knighthood he received just before he left BNFL.

Sir Christopher Harding mixes easily and is a personally charming man who does his homework well before he meets new people, which is very flattering. At BNFL he quickly established himself in the minds of national and local politicians and most sections of the media as someone who could be trusted. It was he who insisted that at least half of BNFL's monthly board meetings should be held close to one of the operating sites and that on the evening before them a dinner should be arranged for local community leaders. At these dinners, he adroitly steered discussion towards the issues then concerning the company, the nuclear industry or the community.

Previously, nearly all board meetings had been held in London, to suit the convenience of the non-executive directors. The executive directors travelled to London on the evening before meetings, dining out in separate, compatible groups. There was little chance for the internal and external directors to get to know each other, let alone members of the local communities, on whom we depended for support.

Christopher Harding also developed the weekend seminars at Sellafield which I instituted at the suggestion of Sir Bernard Ingham. These were held initially at a local hotel some miles away from the site, but Christopher changed the venue to the company's guest house, the Sella Park, on the edge of the site, as a visible expression of our confidence in the safety of the operations carried out at Sellafield.

Our first seminar, hosted by Con, was a crisis event, used to involve Sellafield's main contractors in our fight to re-establish the reputation of the site and protect the THORP project after the Beach Incident. Several of the contractors later created opportunities to issue press statements about the importance of THORP and other major projects to their businesses or wrote to their MPs pointing out how many jobs depended on Sellafield, effectively joining our political lobby operation.

The 'open and honest' public relations strategy developed while Christopher Harding was Chairman placed a great deal of emphasis on the importance of third-party advocacy of this kind and on networking generally. Later seminars, which Christopher or his Chief Executive, Neville Chamberlain, hosted, were devoted to such issues as the role of industry in education, corporate giving, community relations and a range of other subjects designed to show people of influence that at least one nuclear company had normal business interests. Our guests were usually a well-mixed group of people prominent in the field which was to be discussed, together with politicians and local notables and their partners.

Christopher Harding, in particular, always ensured that these weekends were fun as well as useful. The partners of our guests were encouraged to take a full part in the seminar proceedings, but anyone who wanted to skip the Sellafield site visit on Saturday afternoon was provided with an alternative programme – a tour of nearby Muncaster Castle, where the delightful owner, Patrick Gordon Duff Pennington, would declaim his poetry, or to Dove Cottage, where Wordsworth had once lived.

Geoffrey Tucker, a former publicity director of the Conservative Party, had been appointed a consultant to BNFL by Con Allday on the recommendation of Lord McAlpine when BNFL's image was at its lowest ebb after the Beach Incident. I always found Geoffrey's advice invaluable and benefited from his introduction to a much wider circle of influential people than I had been able to reach previously.

Geoffrey, Con Allday (and later Christopher Harding) and I had regular freewheeling discussions, which Geoffrey called 'blue-sky' meetings, at which we bounced ideas off each other about how we could take the company forward. Several important new initiatives were pursued as a result. I remember in particular how we discussed ways of getting the greenhouse effect, caused by burning fossil fuels, on to the political and environmental agenda. We wanted to drive home the message that the UK's nuclear stations saved some fifty million tonnes of carbon dioxide emissions a year. We made the greenhouse effect the talking point of a series of dinners which Geoffrey organized and, whether they were effective or not, it is a fact that shortly after Bernard Ingham, Mrs Thatcher's Chief Press Secretary, had attended one of the dinners, the Prime Minister began to show more interest in the issue.

At several of the blue-sky meetings we also talked about education and my belief that we must capture the minds, if not the hearts, of young children, who were clearly being influenced by the stream of anti-nuclear programmes appearing on television and, it has to be said, by the attitude of many of their teachers. While the nuclear power industry produced literature for schools, it was written by people in the industry without reference to the teaching profession. It was full of jargon, had not been tested for impact and had to be paid for by the schools.

We found a way through that problem later by involving teachers from the North-West, where BNFL has its factories, in our planned educational programme. We were helped considerably when the Government introduced a new school curriculum which required technology to be taught to junior school children. BNFL produced a considerable range of new teaching materials which placed nuclear power in the context of energy as a whole and we were careful not to knock competing sources of power – or not too much. The approach was subtle, almost Jesuitical, and its flavour was captured in the title of the brochure in which we listed what we had on offer: 'For Teachers – By Teachers'. The old arrogance, the assumption that the scientists and engineers of the nuclear power industry knew best, had gone.

One of the things which Geoffrey Tucker's blue-sky meetings did was to make me think back to my early days working for BNFL, when I had insisted that crises involving Sellafield also presented the company with an opportunity, because of the media attention which they attracted. I revived the idea of having a real visitors' centre at Sellafield, not an adjunct to a dental surgery, and discussed my earlier concept with Jeffrey Preece and Bob Cartwright, who had just joined the company as publicity manager on the retirement of Gordon Williams. I also agreed that we should consider using advertising as a way of influencing public opinion and not just helping to sell BNFL's services within a largely captive market.

During these discussions, Geoffrey Tucker told me a story from his days in the advertising industry which struck a chord. Immediately after the war redundant aircraft were available for conversion into passenger-carrying planes and the burgeoning travel industry wanted to develop overseas tourism. But people were afraid of flying – as many still are. The travel industry could have spent its advertising budget trying to convince the public that flying was safe – probably worrying more people than it reassured by doing so – and may even have considered doing so. Instead, it spent its money on showing pictures of the exotic holiday destinations which were being opened up, with their sun-kissed beaches, blue skies and cheap food and drink.

It effectively deflected public attention towards these pleasures and away from the dangers. The travel industry's advertising does exactly the same today. This conversation set me thinking and I agreed with Bob Cartwright and Jeffrey Preece that before we did anything, we must find out what people really thought about Sellafield, our version of the fear of flying.

I told Con Allday what I was doing and gained his support in principle for both strands of the new public relations strategy I was working up – the new exhibition centre and a corporate advertising programme. The proposal to build a new visitors' centre, costing around £5 million, was actually put in the last corporate plan produced by BNFL with Con Allday as its Chairman. He also gave me permission to see if it was possible to work up a proactive advertising campaign.

The corporate plan is the mechanism by which BNFL gains Government support for its fifteen-year rolling programme of capital investment. Unfortunately, the planned expenditure on a new visitors' centre had to be taken out of the plan at the insistence of the civil servants representing the Department of Energy and the Treasury at the corporate plan discussions held at that time.

They said that the then Secretary of State for Energy, Peter Walker, considered the proposals a waste of money. He may also have received protests from the CEGB, as BNFL had tried to load most of the costs of the centre on to the board, its main customer, under the cost plus pricing mechanism then in place, a penny-pinching move by the accountants which I had opposed.

To make matters worse, towards the end of 1985 Con Allday heard that he would have to retire when he reached the age of sixty-five. Con had hoped to become part-time Chairman of the company, but it was not to be. We heard that the Government intended to appoint Christopher Harding as Chairman. He had joined BNFL as a non-executive director in September 1984 on the recommendation of Lord Hanson, with whom he has had a strong business and personal association for many years. Christopher, in turn, had decided to make Neville Chamberlain, who was a divisional director and not on the main BNFL board, his Chief Executive – much to the annoyance of some of the existing executive directors, several of whom had ambitions in that direction themselves.

Unfortunately, we were all aware a good six months before the event that Christopher Harding and Neville Chamberlain were to take up their new appointments as from 1 April 1986. Although Con Allday was still holding the reins, there was a power vacuum and a reluctance to take policy decisions in advance of the new team taking over.

Early in 1986, during this interregnum, there were four incidents at Sellafield in the space of a month, all of them relatively minor but giving the cumulative impression of a site which was out of control. The Heath and Safety Executive's Director, John Rimington, decided that the HSE should carry out a full safety audit of the Sellafield site and for some weeks John and I followed each other into and out of the television studios.

When media interest was at its fiercest, I received a request from Peter Sissons, then covering industry for Channel Four News, for permission to take a television crew up to Sellafield. Peter also asked if Walt Patterson, my old adversary from Friends of the Earth, could join him on the visit and if he could film inside the plutonium store at Sellafield, something no other television programme maker had done. I recommended to Con Allday that we agree to all of Peter Sissons's proposals and he accepted my advice, which helped to overcome opposition from the company's security advisers.

I decided to use the visit by Peter Sissons, who was already an influential television journalist, to reinforce the 'open and honest' impression I had been trying to convey in the radio, television and newspaper interviews I had been giving about the spate of incidents at Sellafield.

Using the freedom which a power vacuum can provide, I made it clear that in future we would accept all requests by journalists for visits to our factories, even when we knew the reporters concerned had an anti-nuclear bias. I also said in public that we would never again refuse to provide someone for radio or television interviews, no matter how strongly we suspected the motives of the producers or interviewers concerned. I knew this meant that some of us would be set up for a public pillorying at times, but felt it was a price which had to be paid if BNFL was to combat the accusations of excessive secrecy and cover-up which once again surrounded its operations at Sellafield.

I had been reinforced in my view that we had to open Sellafield up to the media and the public by the results of the extensive research which we had carried out during much of 1985. The views of the public were extremely worrying and I knew that the series of incidents at Sellafield could only have made the situation worse. I had expected opposition. What was surprising was the overwhelming extent of public antipathy towards the site.

Most people saw BNFL as an environmental polluter and a danger to health, as secretive and, equally damaging, as downright dishonest. Sellafield was regarded as a dangerous place to work or live near. It was glaringly obvious that we would never gain the acceptance of a majority of the public – active support was something we did not even aspire to at that time – unless we communicated more effectively and restored our credibility. I was convinced that effective communications demanded openness, honesty, clarity and a little more humility on the part of everyone from BNFL who was involved in the process. We had to set out to demonstrate this new attitude and we had to use plain language and not jargon. As Bob Williams, a later recruit to BNFL, put it, 'Blinding people with science is as bad as blinding them with silence.'

When Peter Sissons and Walt Patterson arrived at Sellafield at the end of February 1986, they were genuinely surprised at the level of cooperation they received, at a time when a team of inspectors from the Nuclear Installations Inspectorate were still carrying out the formal audit of safety which John Rimington had ordered. There was a real threat of parts of the plant being shut down while improvements were made and we did not hide the fact. The twenty-minute programme which came out of Peter Sissons's visit convinced me that we were on the right lines with our 'open and honest' policy.

Introducing the programme, Peter Sissons described Sellafield as the most controversial nuclear power plant in the world, which – with the exception of Chernobyl – it still is. But he also said that after thirty years of near total secrecy, things were changing and that he had been invited to film anywhere he wanted, subject to the protection of national security. The programme explained reprocessing concisely and effectively and at the end of it Walt Patterson said that he believed that BNFL was now trying to be more open and honest.

There were a couple of unexpected scares as we went round the site filming, but in a strange way they helped to demonstrate that our new policy was for real. As Peter Sissons interviewed Walt and myself outside building B30, where the outer cans are stripped of spent Magnox fuel, a team of workmen wearing full Windscale suits, with separate air supply pipes attached to them, appeared behind us, in camera shot, and barriers were put up where they were to work. Peter asked what was going on and I found out that the workmen were there to repair a pipe which had fractured inside a trench, which they were excavating. The radiation levels must have been fairly high for them to be wearing protective clothing and I said as much on camera, but the fact that we were filming so close to the action put that into perspective.

Peter Sissons also insisted on filming outside the B38 silo building, where there had been the leak which led to the THORP public inquiry, and finally we moved into the plutonium store building. There was nearly an unfortunate moment here too. Peter Sissons was holding a canister of plutonium and was speaking to camera when the canister slipped through his fingers. He caught it in mid-air before it hit the ground.

I persuaded Peter that nothing would have happened if the

canister had crashed to the concrete floor and this piece of film was not used. I even persuaded him to destroy the film so that it would not turn up in one of those programmes showing offcuts of the gaffes occasionally made by TV interviewers and their victims. I hope my confidence in the strength of that canister was not misplaced. I noticed one or two of the people working in the area go a little pale as Peter let it slip through his fingers and a few years later we had a scare about the condition of some of the containers, which began to bulge as a result of a build-up of gases and had to be repackaged to ensure their integrity.

It was probably the interest created by the Channel Four News report which encouraged Charles Stewart, an independent television producer specializing in 'fly on the wall' programmes, to seek permission to make a documentary showing day-to-day working life at Sellafield, to be filmed over a period of several months. Charles had recently made a film about the operation of a police force in the south of England which had received a lot of publicity because it led to two policemen having to resign when it was shown. They had been filmed interviewing a woman who had been raped – and giving her a hard time.

Gordon Steele, the head of the Sellafield site, informed Christopher Harding that the management and trade unions at Sellafield were unanimously opposed to Charles Stewart being allowed to film at the site. I told Christopher that I did not believe we had a choice, given our stated policy. We could not be open and honest when we felt like it and closed and dishonest at other times. It was all or nothing. Christopher sympathized with what I was saying, but told me that he was not prepared to overrule Gordon Steele. I was told that if I felt so strongly I would have to go to Sellafield and get the management and trade unions to change their minds. I decided to try to do just that, having come to the conclusion that if I failed I would resign. This was no big deal – the open and honest campaign and my frequent television appearances defending Sellafield were attracting attention and I had several tentative job offers in my pocket.

At separate meetings I found that the management and workforce at Sellafield were not as opposed to Charles Stewart filming there as Christopher Harding had been led to believe. My argument that we could not be open and honest intermittently was well received and I explained that the 'fly on the wall' filming technique did not mean that there would be tiny cameras hidden round the site filming every movement and miniature microphones picking up every unguarded statement. There would be one camera crew, and their equipment would be obvious.

If anyone decided to break the rules by ignoring safety procedures and was filmed doing so, or said something outrageous, he or she deserved to be disciplined, I said. The filming went ahead. It was later shown on Channel Four, lasting over an hour and a half, and did a great deal to demystify what goes on at Sellafield. Nobody was disciplined as a result of the programme and nobody lost their job. Our new public information policy remained intact, and I soldiered on at BNFL.

At the time of the Peter Sissons news programme we were nearly ready to launch the advertisements which formed the other main plank of our 'open and honest' campaign. They were developed for us by Young and Rubicam, the agency which I had chosen, in consultation with Jeffrey Preece and Bob Cartwright, because I was impressed by the depth of the analysis it carried out into BNFL's problems The possibility of using advertising to help mould public opinion in support of nuclear power was not one which appealed to everyone. Bernard Ingham, for example, who was then still at No. 10, was firmly opposed to the idea, largely because Ken Livingstone was using advertising at that time in support of his unsuccessful campaign to keep the Greater London Council in being. Bernard did not want to see political advertising on the American scale in the UK and I could understand his concern. I did point out, however, that whenever an industry was about to be privatized – surely a political act – we would suddenly see an extensive advertising campaign extolling the virtues of that industry.

Instead of grouping prospective audiences according to their spending power, Young and Rubicam concentrated more on the attitudes of particular groups. They had also carried out research which showed that most people reach particular opinions on the basis of the impressions they receive, rather than by sifting factual information, most of which is not absorbed. This was something I had long suspected.

I remembered taking part in a Border television programme in Cumbria some years earlier when a local GP, Barry Walker, deeply concerned that Sellafield might have caused childhood leukaemias in his area, was sufficiently overcome that he started to weep. I saw a video of that programme later and came to the conclusion that from the moment Dr Walker started to cry, anything I said would have been forgotten.

I was persuaded by John Banks and Toby Hoare, the Young & Rubicam executives handling the BNFL account, that we stood no chance of influencing the attitudes of people who were extremely anti-nuclear through advertising, so we should not waste money trying to do so. We had to concentrate on three key groups of people who might listen to what we said and whom we might convince that we had a case worth supporting.

The first of these groups was categorized as the 'mainstreamer', people best thought of as Mr and Mrs Average – home-centred, patriotic, the core of our society. This was the group John Major probably tried to reach through his 'back to basics' campaign, although that lacked the subtlety of the Sellafield strategy and, of course, failed. The 'mainstreamers' were people who did not fully understand the issues, but worried about leaks and accidents and how these might affect their own well-being.

The second target group was categorized as the 'succeeders'

– business people who were generally well informed and confident, and represented the commercial thrust of society. They could be expected to want Britain to be at the forefront of a world technology such as nuclear power.

Finally, there were the 'reformers' – highly educated people who were more concerned with social and moral issues than other people – *Guardian* readers, if you will. That may seem surprising, but we felt that these people would be interested in such issues as the effect which burning fossil fuels had on the environment and how the energy requirements of the developing countries were to be met if their conditions were to be improved. Together, the 'succeeders' and the 'reformers' formed a group of people who, for different reasons, were more likely to take action than others.

Through advertising we wanted people to come to accept that BNFL was not trying to hide anything, rather that it was going to great lengths to provide facts and information to the public. We also wanted to show that the company was confident that once people had all the facts, they would be reassured about the professionalism, safety and benefits of the work which BNFL did for Britain. The strategy we settled upon was straightforward. For 'mainstreamers' we intended to use television to communicate the 'open and honest' concept in a simple way. For 'succeeders' and 'reformers' this would be supported by a press campaign designed to fill in more detail, recognizing their role in society as influential opinion-formers.

To a considerable extent the nature and subject of the launch commercial for television were dictated to us by the then Independent Broadcasting Association (IBA). The IBA's Code of Advertising Standards and Practice at that time stated that 'no advertisement may be inserted by or on behalf of any body, the objects whereof are wholly or mainly of a political nature and no advertisement may be directed towards any political end'. In response to requests for clarification of this rule made by Young and Rubicam, the IBA stipulated that 'advertising cannot make a case for nuclear energy and due impartiality must be preserved on the part of the advertiser on matters of political or industrial controversy or relating to public policy'.

How the Greater London Council and privatization ads got through the IBA sieve I do not know, but BNFL was extremely tightly constrained and several advertising concepts were turned down as Young & Rubicam struggled to get BNFL and Sellafield accepted. In the end the IBA insisted that to meet its rules advertising had to be associated with the sale of products and should not be used to influence attitudes. As BNFL did not have a product which was for general sale, it would not be allowed on to television, we were told.

However, this interpretation of the rules provided Young & Rubicam with the way forward. BNFL did have a product which was available to everybody – the small exhibition centre over the dental surgery close to Sellafield which I had managed to get built when I first joined BNFL. It was a tourist attraction of sorts – and other tourist attractions were being advertised. The IBA could wriggle no further. Fortunately, using the exhibition centre as a focus for our television advertising fitted in remarkably well with the results of our research. We had tested advertisements which sought to explain the benefits of nuclear power and others which discussed the risks, trying to put them into the context of everyday risks, and they simply did not work. BNFL's credibility was so low that nobody believed what we said. The only message which did register favourably with our test audiences was the one which invited people to go to Sellafield to see what went on there for themselves.

The launch commercial which Young and Rubicam developed within the IBA rules and in response to the results of our test programme was to the point. Against a backdrop of the Cumbrian countryside, beautifully filmed, an open invitation was to be extended to everyone to visit the Sellafield exhibition centre. This was to be accompanied by press advertisements containing a similar message, which would be placed in a selection of Sunday newspaper colour supplements and other magazines. A formal invitation card was attached to the advertisement, inviting people to visit the exhibition centre. When the card was removed it revealed a picture of Sellafield, looking at its best on a sunny day in the Lake District.

This was the advertising campaign which we were ready to launch early in 1986 – as soon as I could obtain BNFL board approval to spend nearly £3 million on it, a tremendous sum for anything to do with public relations at that time but small beer by comparison with the business I was trying to protect. Con Allday was unwilling to take my proposal to the board so close to his retirement; I had to brief Christopher Harding and try to gain his support so that we could launch as soon as he took over the chairmanship in April.

In April 1986 the Chernobyl disaster happened, throwing the nuclear industry into turmoil as the radioactive cloud from the Ukraine moved across Sweden, where it was first identified for the Western world, and towards Britain. It arrived over the UK early one evening, as Christopher Harding was hosting a 'come and meet the new Chairman' cocktail party for senior BNFL staff and their partners at Risley. I had not seen much of my wife for some weeks, because of all the radio and television interviews I had to give during the spate of incidents at Sellafield. Sheila and I were looking forward to a relaxing evening and an early night.

Shortly after six p.m. I was called to the telephone, just as I reached for my first gin and tonic. It was the duty officer at Sellafield. He informed me that the Chernobyl cloud had arrived at Sellafield, of all places. I was told that the radiation levels from the fall-out washed by the rain on to the clothes of workers as they entered the plant were so high that they had triggered off the installed alarms. These alarms were intended to register contamination on the working clothes of people about to leave the factory, not entering it. A senior member of Sellafield's environmental staff had also measured the radioactivity with a geiger counter which he kept at his home near Cockermouth, well away from Sellafield.

Sellafield wanted to issue a press statement that it had measured the effects of Chernobyl, to show how sensitive its radiation detection instruments were. After my experience of a succession of leaks from the site over the previous weeks, I asked the duty officer how sure he was that the radiation being measured was not the result of yet another Sellafield mistake. He assured me that the material was from Chernobyl. Nevertheless, I refused permission for Sellafield to make a press announcement immediately and told the duty officer to carry out more checks and to wait for me to call back.

What I was worried about was that because we were close to deadlines for the evening news on television and for the first editions of the next day's national newspapers, Sellafield's name would become associated with what had happened at Chernobyl – the last thing I wanted. I did not allow Sellafield to make a statement until after I had heard on the radio that the UKAEA site at Winfrith had announced the arrival of the Chernobyl contamination in Dorset, at the other end of the country, claiming to be the first to spot it. In fact, of course, it was another Sellafield first. As it was, Cumbria suffered more than most other areas from the effects of the Chernobyl fall-out, which still persist in some parts of the country. There are also a few west Cumbrian farmers who continue to believe, quite erroneously, that Sellafield discharged something nasty into the environment on the night that the Chernobyl fall-out arrived.

The Chernobyl disaster made me question whether I wanted to continue working in an industry where such a thing could happen, and I am sure that many others began to have doubts too. I was forced to consider my position quickly as I was committed to speaking at a conference on nuclear power at Lancaster University a few weeks later. I had been invited by Dr Brian Wynne, someone whom I had first met when he appeared as an objector at the THORP public inquiry. Brian has written extensively about science and technology and their associated risks, as well as about public understanding of these issues, and he is someone whose work I respect.

I threw away the speech I had prepared for the conference and wrote another on what I thought would or should happen in the wake of Chernobyl. I came to the conclusion that nuclear power would continue, despite the public clamour for it to be halted, because it was needed, certainly in those countries which were heavily dependent on it, such as France, Japan and, incredibly perhaps, the Soviet Union and its Eastern European satellites. If that judgement was correct, I argued, then those employed in the world-wide nuclear industry must do all they could to ensure that another Chernobyl could not happen. If Chernobyl was the result of inferior technology, as Walter Marshall, then the Chairman of the CEGB, insisted, then it was in the interest of the West to improve that technology, without too much concern for cost.

Lord Marshall told the media that Britain had repeatedly warned the Russians that reactors such as that built at Chernobyl would not be considered safe enough to be licensed in Britain. That is as may be. It seems to me that the warning must have been whispered to scientists working in the Russian nuclear industry. It had certainly never reached my ears.

What I did not tell the Lancaster University conference was that by then Lord Marshall had convinced himself that the highly vocal public opposition to nuclear power which had followed Chernobyl could only be silenced by sacrificing one of the UK's older Magnox nuclear power stations. He suggested that BNFL should volunteer to shut down Calder Hall, as it was the oldest station. We pointed out that shutting down Calder Hall, which provided steam and electricity supplies at Sellafield, would bring reprocessing to a halt. Lord Marshall then began to think of other potential targets for closure, including some of the CEGB's own stations. I was a member of the industry group chaired by Lord Marshall which was looking at a series of issues related to Chernobyl, including the political fall-out of this horrendous event. I argued that the anti-nuclear activists would not be satisfied with the sacrifice of one station. Scenting blood, they would want more.

It was Neville Chamberlain who won the argument, however. He pointed out that shutting down one nuclear power station would have a domino effect, bringing the operation of all the stations into question as fuel and reprocessing costs were spread over fewer and fewer stations. A precipitate and unmanaged closure programme would damage the economics of nuclear power, Neville insisted. The force of his argument and the determination with which he pursued it prevailed. He now has the chance to prove his argument further with the Government's decision to hand the Magnox closure programme over to BNFL.

At Brian Wynne's conference I expanded on Neville Chamberlain's argument that even if the illogical decision was taken to close the UK nuclear industry down because of an accident elsewhere in the world involving a form of technology not used in the UK, the shutdown process itself would have to be carefully managed if it was to be safe. I may have persuaded a few of the local authority representatives for whom the conference was primarily intended that there was some sort of future for nuclear power, but I failed miserably with the student demonstrators who were allowed into the conference. As I spoke they moved slowly around the hall, their faces painted white and some of them carrying babies, and from time to time a few of them would fall to the floor, simulating what they imagined were the death throes of someone dying from radiation.

With stories about the effects of Chernobyl still appearing in the newspapers, alongside heavy criticism of the way the Government had handled the communications associated with the crisis, I now had to decide what to do about BNFL's planned advertising campaign, which was ready to be launched. I came to the conclusion that we should go ahead with it immediately and went to see Christopher Harding. I told him that I believed members of the public wanted more than ever before to understand nuclear power. They would either throw it out as a result of Chernobyl or come to terms with it.

We launched the campaign just six weeks after Chernobyl – and it was an immediate success. An effective press relations operation ensured that the first television advertisement was carried as a news item on virtually every BBC and commercial television news bulletin and every national newspaper ran a piece about the launch. The BBC incorporated the fifty-second ad into its main TV news programmes – surely the first and last time it has carried an advertisement for anything other than its own programmes or publications. We calculated later that the advertisements generated more than £2 million of free advertising in newspaper editorial columns and radio and television news slots, plus a wider range of spin-off newspaper articles and visits to Sellafield by journalists and TV news crews.

Our appeal to people to visit the exhibition centre did more than reinforce our message that we wanted to be open and honest, although we know from follow-up research that it worked very well in that context. The important thing was not how many people actually went up to Sellafield but that most of the population now knew they could go there. Later we found that the television advertisement also carried a subliminal message on safety. People began to say that Sellafield must be safe or BNFL would not have dared to invite people to visit the site.

The success of the campaign infuriated Greenpeace, which complained about the advertising being a waste of public funds, which should have been spent on safety. This gave us the opportunity to get the media interested in just how much we had spent on safety and the environment and on the fact that, far from wasting public funds, BNFL had paid a dividend to the Treasury practically every year since the company was formed. Greenpeace took some time to recognize that it was counter-productive to complain about BNFL trying to inform the public about Sellafield's activities. We were now setting the agenda and were sufficiently confident that we were on the right lines that we began to tweak Greenpeace's tail a little in some of our advertising.

I remember one advertisement which Young and Rubicam produced in particular. We took two facing pages in most of the national newspapers. On the left-hand page we ran these words: 'For one side of the argument about nuclear energy British Nuclear Fuels urge you to write to this address.' We then gave BNFL's address. On the opposite, right-hand page we ran exactly the same words – and gave Greenpeace's address, using their logo. The message was clear – we believed our arguments were more persuasive than theirs and were prepared to take our chances. Greenpeace was silly enough to complain to the press that we had used their name and logo without permission. All that did was draw more attention to the advertisement, giving us even more publicity.

We reinforced the central message that we wanted people to come to Sellafield with a number of special events, most of them the idea of Bob Cartwright, a talented publicity manager who was later poached from BNFL by the brewing industry. Bob organized a series of five rail trips to Sellafield from all over the country, using trains pulled by Britain's most famous steam locomotive, the Flying Scotsman. The trips were used in the new press advertising and also attracted many news stories. We did not want visitors to treat their trip to Sellafield as just another way to fill a rainy day in the Lake District, however. We wanted them to learn about nuclear power, radiation, radioactive waste and reprocessing.

It was soon apparent that the second-floor exhibition centre was far too small for either purpose, so we bought two attractive 'Sellafield Sightseer' coaches, equipped them with video monitors and ran trips around the site, easing the log-jam at the centre itself. As the coaches stopped outside a particular building, the video monitors played a tape describing what went on inside it.

As a result of the advertising campaign the number of visitors to Sellafield increased dramatically, from just under 30,000 visitors in 1985 to 65,000 in 1986. By 1987, the first full year of advertising, they had reached 104,000 and the tiny exhibition centre over the dentist's surgery was bursting at the seams. In May 1987 I went back to the BNFL board for more money and received permission to build a new Sellafield visitors' centre, at a cost of £5 million.

The money was split roughly equally between the fabric of the new building and the display materials inside it. We decided that the centre must house a 'state of the art' exhibition, with working models such as a simulated full-sized nuclear reactor core, with operating control rods and fuel elements, and a fission tunnel (known to the staff as the tunnel of love), with thousands of lights and mirrors creating an image of the nuclear chain reaction.

I wanted people to be able to use geiger counters to measure the radiation given off particular materials, including some in daily use in their homes. Almost everything in the exhibition was to be audio-visually based, as I was convinced that people needed to be entertained while they were being educated, that impressions were more important than the written word for most people.

We also provided a team of information guides to answer any questions visitors might have and, in all, we ensured that the new visitors' centre had full tourist facilities, right down to award-winning loos. We wanted people to enjoy the Sellafield experience and incorporated a 140-seater coffee shop and restaurant, with a splendid view over the Sellafield site and round towards the fells. We even put in a shop, selling an ever-increasing range of Sellafield souvenirs, including 'Mighty Atom' toys and sticks of rock with the name Sellafield running through them. The turnover of that shop is now over a quarter of a million pounds a year.

From planning permission in 1987, the visitors' centre was built and opened twelve months later in 1988. All was completed a good twelve hours before the official opening by the Duke of Edinburgh in June 1988. The number of visitors soared to 160,000 over the next year and, in 1989, the centre and BNFL's overall 'open and honest' public information policy won the top Institute of Public Relations award, the sword of Excellence.

The Sellafield's visitors' centre and its associated advertising campaign have benefited not only BNFL but also people living and working in the local community, who had long felt that the adverse publicity attracted by Sellafield had damaged tourism in the North-West and Lakes areas, and turned them into pariahs.

Chapter Eight

Community Relations:

Big Brother Dependency

For nearly half a century the people of west Cumbria have given tremendous public support to Sellafield, despite the somewhat mixed feelings about the place many of them express in private. This has been invaluable to BNFL, particularly when the continued operation of its largest site has come into question following a major incident. For good or ill, Sellafield has an impact on most aspects of economic, social and political life in the area. I tried to repay some of the loyalty shown to the site by persuading the BNFL board to invest in a comprehensive programme of community support in the mid-1980s. The structure which was created as a result of that initiative is still in place today, regarded by the European Union as a model of its kind.

The proposal which I put to the BNFL board was not inspired by altruism. In order to protect a valuable asset, local loyalty, I regarded it as essential for the company to prepare well in advance for the time when THORP and the other major construction projects at Sellafield were finished, throwing thousands of people out of work, rather than to wait until after the event, as happened when the coal, iron and steel industries abandoned west Cumbria. That day has come with a vengeance. The area faces a distinctly uncomfortable future.

A decade ago some of my BNFL board colleagues were strongly opposed to what I was trying to do. They argued that it was enough that the company provided much of the west Cumbrian population with a living and paid substantial rates into the area. I could understand the argument, but not accept it. I had no doubt that without a strong measure of local support, Sellafield would be in real trouble. As it is, it will be difficult for BNFL to retain the area's goodwill as it sheds labour over the next five years and unemployment rises.

At the peak, Sellafield employed more than 8,000 people on the operating plants and there were another 7,500 workers employed on the construction of THORP, more than half of them local people. At current money values, I estimate that the Sellafield wages bill was around £200 million a year at that time, a tremendously important factor in the local economy.

The position today is very different. THORP and its associated plants employ around 2,000 people – 5,500 fewer than worked on their construction for some years. And the rest of the Sellafield workforce, already down to 6,600 in 1995 from the peak figure of 8,000, is set to decline by a further 2,000 by the year 2000 under a redundancy programme announced by BNFL in 1994, which the company hopes to achieve through voluntary wastage.

The sum effect is that by the end of this decade Sellafield will be providing work for less than half the number of local people that it employed during the boom years. The position is likely to worsen as the old Calder Hall Magnox power station is shut down early next century, to be replaced by a gas-fired power station supplying electricity and steam to

Sellafield. Even so, Sellafield will still be by far the biggest single employer in west Cumbria unless something dramatic happens elsewhere in the business community.

Despite the disruption which was caused, the nuclear power industry was welcomed into west Cumbria with open arms when it arrived in the late 1940s. It is easy to see why. Apart from agriculture and fishing, the area had been heavily dependent since the seventeenth century on industries which were no longer capable of supporting the community – coal, iron, steel and shipbuilding. Since the mid-1930s west Cumbria had suffered from unemployment levels which were far higher than the national average and the area had the doubtful distinction of being one of the first in the UK to receive special regional assistance. A few small businesses were encouraged to move into the area as a result of that help, only to leave again once it was removed.

With a history of industrial depression and neglect, the coming of nuclear power was seen as the salvation of west Cumbria, particularly when the industry began its association with electricity generation in the 1960s and started to lose its dependence on the production of materials for the nuclear weapons programme. I believe that the loyalty which the people of the area have shown towards Sellafield grew out of the sense of relief which the region felt when the site started to develop as its only substantial employment lifeline.

While I was with BNFL I also liked to believe that local people continued to support Sellafield when things went wrong because they understood the real rather than imagined dangers of nuclear power and had confidence in the scientists and engineers who ran the site. That is certainly what the people running Sellafield claimed. I now know that the loyalty of the majority of the people of west Cumbria stems purely and simply from their recognition that it is not in their interest to bite the hand that feeds them. Because of their long association with the coal industry, which has claimed over 500 lives in west Cumbria over the last century, they are also aware that no industry can be totally safe.

My own association with west Cumbria and knowledge of its needs began at the time of the THORP public inquiry, which I attended nearly every day, using some of the evenings to get to know the area. Much of it is very beautiful, with considerable untapped tourist potential, more attractive, I find, than the better-known Lake District beauty spots to the east. But there is dereliction and poor housing too, particularly along the coastal strip between Sellafield and Workington.

As part of its application for planning permission to build THORP, BNFL negotiated a package of planning gain aid to the region, recognizing for the first time that major industrial development brought with it environmental detriment as well as economic advantage. My predecessor as BNFL's Company Secretary, Arthur Scott, negotiated this agreement with Copeland Borough Council and Cumbria County Council. The Government chipped in with a promise to build a bypass at Egremont – and took well over a decade to do so, completing it only after the main construction work on THORP was finished.

The planning gain assistance associated with THORP is said to have cost BNFL over £22 million, but it would be wrong to believe that the expenditure represented corporate generosity. Most of the spending was as much in BNFL's interest as that of the local community. I inherited responsibility for the programme, which took from 1976 to 1983 to complete. It included improvements to the town centre of Whitehaven, through the renovation of sixty attractive Georgian properties which had fallen into decay; road, rail and sewerage improvements at or near to Sellafield; construction of a 250–bed hostel for BNFL staff helping to design and construct THORP; landscaping at Sellafield; the construction of a new training centre for apprentices; and a relatively small grant to the Copeland local authority for recreational facilities.

All of this work was just about completed when the 1983

Beach Incident occurred, damaging the tourist industry in west Cumbria and angering people who could normally be relied upon to shrug off any national publicity about incidents at Sellafield as probably exaggerated. Communications with the local community were particularly difficult, because it took six months to restore the use of local beaches after the incident.

Initially, it was the belief that a cover-up had taken place which upset members of the Sellafield Local Liaison Committee, the formal communications channel with the local community. Then the site management's attempt to keep the workforce briefed on a developing situation went badly wrong. Many thousands of employees, working different shift patterns, had to be kept informed and it sometimes took several days to brief on a particular issue. Inevitably the message passed to different groups changed with time and when the groups exchanged notes, the suspicion grew that management was being evasive and trying to mislead.

BNFL came under renewed pressure to help the community and eventually agreed to do so. I led the BNFL team involved in the discussions which went on at that time, cementing my position at the centre of BNFL's community relations activity, primarily at Sellafield but also close to the company's other factories. There was nothing structured about the way we handled the demands for help which poured in from local authorities, tourist organizations and individuals. We simply gave in when the pressure seemed too great to resist.

Most of the benefit went to Copeland, the local authority worst affected by the Beach Incident, in response to special pleading from the authority itself, from members of the Sellafield workforce who held various offices in the local community or from Jack Cunningham. Between 1984 and 1988 BNFL helped with the cost of renovating Whitehaven Town Hall, sponsored a pro-am golf tournament at Seascale and other sports activities, put money into the Whitehaven Rugby League Club and instituted and sponsored a Whitehaven Heritage Award scheme, aimed at encouraging local business interests in the town to restore their premises, most of which looked distinctly run-down. We bought our way back into some sort of favour.

I was also persuaded by Jack Cunningham that BNFL should provide most of the money for an all-weather athletics track which was built at Whitehaven. I saw this as a public relations opportunity and wanted the company to finance a track capable of attracting international events and provide training facilities which might help Cumbrian athletes to reach international standard. I believed that a successful track would help to promote the impression that west Cumbria is a healthy place in which to live and work.

The benefits provided to Copeland were supplemented by support for Allerdale, the next-door local authority, which covers Workington and Maryport, as well as projects put forward by Cumbria County Council. In the rest of Cumbria, BNFL provided grants to the County Council for an archaeological dig at a Roman site at Birdoswald (still a developing tourist attraction) and for a health centre. In addition, the company started to sponsor the Lowther horse trials, on Lord Lonsdale's estate, which it continued to do for several years. The Lowther trials had Prince Philip as a competitor and this enabled Christopher Harding, BNFL's Chairman at that time, to meet His Royal Highness, providing him with the opportunity to persuade Prince Philip to open the Sellafield visitors' centre in 1985 – a tremendous boost to site morale.

The Lowther horse trials also had a tangible public relations benefit on the eastern side of the county, well away from Sellafield, where many of Sellafield's sternest Cumbrian critics live. For this reason I would have kept the sponsorship going, but it was cancelled on the instructions of Neville Chamberlain, BNFL's Chief Executive, who believes in sponsorships rotating. I prefer to stick with winners once they have been identified, for as long as they remain successful.

In all, BNFL spent over £3 million on community projects

in west Cumbria between 1984 and 1988. I was not convinced that it was right for a major company to continue to behave in this paternalistic way, responding only when sufficient pressure was applied in the aftermath of a particular incident at Sellafield or when a sensitive planning application was held up by Copeland Borough Council. Delays, or threatened delays, in dealing with planning applications for new plants, some of them said by the Sellafield management to be on a tight critical path, was the main mechanism Copeland had for squeezing the last drop of financial support out of BNFL.

I wanted the local community to join BNFL in developing a longer-term approach towards community support, one which recognized west Cumbria's need for a wider, more diverse industrial base. Jimmy Johnston, then leader of Copeland Council, shared my view and together we began to discuss how best BNFL could structure its community support. Like me, Jimmy believed very strongly that what was needed was some form of partnership between the company and the community, not grace and favour largesse from Big Brother Sellafield. We also involved two very able local authority planning officers in discussions of the practicalities of what we had in mind, Bob Metcalfe of Copeland and John Burnett, who went on to become Chief Executive of Cumbria County Council.

It was John Wills, a non-executive director of BNFL at that time, who first warned me of the danger of the company acting like Big Brother in Cumbria, where there was – and still is – a great deal of sensitivity about the dominance of BNFL in the local community, not least in local politics, because of the politically active Sellafield workforce. John lived in the county and had a good understanding of local attitudes. He advised me that the people of Cumbria knew only too well how dependent the county was on Sellafield and did not like to be reminded of the fact continually, particularly if they did not work at the plant, lived on the far side of the county or made their living out of tourism, agriculture and fishing.

John Wills was Chairman of Enterprise West Cumbria, a small industrial development agency, formed with support from British Coal and British Steel when thousands of people were made redundant as pits and steelworks were shut down in the late 1970s and early 1980s. The agency also had local authority assistance. I discussed with John my feeling that BNFL must do something about its known redundancies before, rather than after, the event. Together we persuaded Christopher Harding and Neville Chamberlain that the company should join Enterprise West Cumbria, although I felt that it was not really the vehicle for community support which BNFL needed, as it concentrated its efforts on attracting inward investment into Allerdale, which at that time benefited from Assisted Area Status and was therefore most likely to have some success.

Copeland, because of the employment provided by Sellafield, did not have this status and Jimmy Johnston and other Copeland councillors were not too happy about BNFL, with its biggest factory in their area, helping the neighbouring borough of Allerdale attract new businesses, possibly at Copeland's expense. I soon came to the conclusion that if BNFL was to make a continuing contribution towards job creation, something other than Enterprise West Cumbria was needed.

In 1987 I commissioned a study into possible ways forward. We were fortunate that the study team was led by Professor John Fyfe, who has a world-wide reputation in this field and an ability to get on with people. This is essential when someone tries to bring about change in a small, often divided, community. To an extent, the study was constrained by Neville Chamberlain's insistence that any money put into a new initiative should be kept under BNFL's effective control. This annoyed the Cumbrian local authorities, which intended to put the smaller, but still significant, sums they had available into the same pot, as did British Coal, British Steel and other minor contributors. I shared Neville's concerns, but accommodating them made it extremely difficult for John

Fyfe and his colleagues to come up with an organizational formula which satisfied everyone.

Eventually, in late 1987, two organizations were formed. The West Cumbria Development Fund (WCDF), with a board consisting of representatives of the main financial contributors, was made responsible for the overall management and allocation of financial resources. BNFL agreed to provide up to £1 million a year for ten years to the fund. This sounds generous, but it must be remembered that since 1976 the company had ploughed an average of £2 million a year into the area, without much control over how it was spent.

I was asked by some of the local authority representatives if I would become the first Chairman of the WCDF. I told them they should invite Neville Chamberlain to take the post, recognizing the personal effort he had put into getting the project through the BNFL board, in the face of some opposition. I also thought that becoming Chairman would lock him into the initiative and demonstrate the importance BNFL attached to it. I succeeded Neville as Chairman in 1990.

In parallel with the WCDF we established the West Cumbria Development Agency (WCDA), which was intended to be the executive arm of the initiative. Its main role was to help create and develop small businesses and to promote large-scale corporate and industrial developments in West Cumbria. The WCDA was kept separate from the WCDF but relied on it to meet its day-to-day running costs and to provide the capital it needed to support new ventures. The WCDA was encouraged to extend and develop its role from the original small-scale business development activities which it inherited from the old Enterprise West Cumbria operation and to become the primary action-oriented agency of the two-part initiative. It was told to involve itself in providing assistance to existing firms, to identify local entrepreneurs and to help them get their business ideas off the ground. It was also expected to provide resource packaging assistance and advice to companies considering moving into the area and to be responsible for property management and development.

The WCDF was given a commercial budget, to be used for supporting existing or new business developments through venture capital loans, equity participation or loan guarantees. It had to try to obtain a reasonable return on the money it invested, with the objective of achieving earnings which would enable the fund to become self-supporting eventually – an extremely optimistic target. It was also agreed that the WCDF should be the vehicle for developing a science and technology park in west Cumbria, which it was hoped would become an international centre of excellence for scientific, engineering and technologically oriented research and development.

At some risk of the company becoming further identified as the Big Brother of the area, the Fyfe Report also recommended that BNFL should do far more through its purchasing power to help promote the development of supplier firms in west Cumbria, helping to create more jobs locally. It was felt that BNFL should not just support local concerns but take a more positive role by helping local firms to understand more about the company's requirements and by developing suitable standards and specifications, perhaps with some funding to help local firms get under way. Finally, it was thought that BNFL could do something to assist the area by mentioning the development potential of west Cumbria to any of its customers in Europe, the Far East and the US who might be thinking of establishing operations in the UK.

The Fyfe Report's proposals were very ambitious and it was doubtful whether they could all be brought to fruition. As might have been expected, there was a great deal of internal rivalry between the people running the WCDA and the staff of the WCDF, who were mainly provided by BNFL. Inevitably, there was some duplication of functions. It also has to be said that in the early years far too much money was approved by both the agency and the fund for 'lost causes', lame-duck companies which were supported for short-term political reasons rather than because they had any real chance of success in employment terms.

One of my last acts as Chairman of the WCDF was to commission John Fyfe to take another look at the structure of the joint initiative and in particular at the relationship between the WCDA and the WCDF. It came as no great surprise to me when he recommended that the two bodies be amalgamated into one. The new organization formed as a result, known as the West Cumbria Partnership, had not really had time to bed down when I resigned in 1994, but I understand that it is doing well now and that the internal wrangling has eased.

Despite its problems, what we put in place to help the local community in west Cumbria has had its successes. BNFL has increased the volume of goods and services purchased from suppliers in the area substantially, partly by moving the relevant section of its massive purchasing department from Risley to Sellafield. At the peak in 1993, Sellafield was buying about £70 million worth of goods and services locally each year. Unfortunately for the area, this figure has fallen considerably with the end of the major construction programme at the site. Somewhat late in the day, there has also been some success with the technology spin-off programme which Sellafield agreed to try to develop in response to another recommendation in the Fyfe Report.

The most successful project to be undertaken by the WCDF, however, is the one which I least expected to succeed. I simply could not see the isolated west Cumbrian community being capable of hosting an internationally recognized centre of scientific and technological excellence. I now believe that this will happen with time. Credit for the success of the Westlakes Science and Technology Park, which has attracted funding from the European Union (EU) and from the Rural Development Commission, must go to Neville Chamberlain, who had not only the vision to see the potential of this ambitious venture but also the imagination and drive to make things happen.

Westlakes has three major areas of development: the Geoffrey Schofield Laboratories, so named to commemorate a former BNFL Chief Medical Officer; the Research Institute; and business units and support services, which are built as companies are attracted into the area. BNFL demonstrated its commitment to the laboratories early on by relocating some of its personnel there from Sellafield. As well as supporting operations at Sellafield, the laboratories offer external services and have a link with local schools, providing places for trainees and work experience for sixth-form college students.

Westlakes could not have been the success it now seems likely to be without the Objective Two development support it has been given by the EU. So far west Cumbria has received over £10 million from the EU and it is currently seeking more funding from that source, including an application for a European Development Fund grant of £1.5 million. This would cover half the capital cost of the proposed construction of an International Research and Graduate Centre, which it is planned to incorporate into the Westlakes Research Institute development now taking shape on the Westlakes campus, under the direction of Professor Derek Ellwood, the Chief Executive of the Research Institute, and Tim Knowles, General Manager of the Science and Technology Park.

There is even the possibility that the Research and Graduate Centre could become one of the building blocks of the 'University of the Lakes' which has been advocated for Cumbria by Dale Campbell-Savours, Labour MP for Workington. Dale's vision is of a multi-sited university, building on and enhancing provision in existing institutions of further and higher education in the county. The establishment of such a university, hopefully centred on west Cumbria as much as possible, would give a tremendous fillip to higher education in a part of the world which has been deprived of decent facilities for far too long.

In addition to persuading the BNFL board that the company must provide the Sellafield area with some sort of cushion against the devastating unemployment effects which were coming, I also tried to get the Government to recognize the problem during the 1980s. I joined the local authorities of Cumbria in several attempts to convince civil servants and ministers that west Cumbria was providing a service to the nation by accepting reprocessing and nuclear waste at Sellafield and that this should be recognized and rewarded by substantial Government investment in transport and other infrastructure and social improvements. This is desperately needed if the area is to diversify its economic base. We got nowhere with Whitehall.

The response from the relevant Government departments – primarily the Department of the Environment and the Ministry of Transport, but also BNFL's sponsor at that time, the Department of Energy, now absorbed into the Department of Trade and Industry – was that west Cumbria had Sellafield and should look in that direction for help. They said as much publicly, throwing an additional burden of expectation on to BNFL and increasing the sense of dependency on the Sellafield site which local people already felt.

I am sure that the local authorities will try to use the Nirex waste repository project as a lever to obtain Government support for the area, if that scheme goes ahead, and who can blame them? In the US the Government agency charged with the task of obtaining local agreement to the establishment of a nuclear waste repository has been given a virtually open chequebook for the task. But based on my experience, nobody can be too hopeful about Cumbria's chances of success in distant Whitehall. I have to say too that the local perception is that Nirex is not doing enough to assist the local authorities to lobby central Government for improvements.

The Government not only failed to help west Cumbria prepare for the future during the 1980s but actually reduced the assistance provided to the Whitehaven Travel to Work

Area (TTWA), the main beneficiary of employment created by Sellafield, during the THORP construction programme. Although that programme was obviously of limited duration, Whitehaven TTWA found that it was no longer eligible for Regional Development Grants, for help from the European Development Fund or for other forms of selective financial assistance under the provisions of the Industrial Development Act.

Worse than that, because of the way central Government funding for local authorities works, the borough of Copeland – which includes the Whitehaven TTWA – gained no real benefit from BNFL when the company's rates bill rose with the introduction of massive new plants such as THORP. Until 1991, a couple of years before THORP started up, all the business rates paid by BNFL went to Copeland and to Cumbria County Council, which provides education and social services to west Cumbria along with the rest of the county. Then the Unified Business Rate system was introduced, under which the Government determines the rate poundage and the local authority collects the money, passing it all on to the Government for disbursement.

The amount of money which local authorities receive back and are therefore allowed to spend (the Standard Spending Assessment) is subject to a formula devised by the Government, with weightings based on such factors as population density, unemployment levels, the prevalence of ethnic minorities and the length of an area's coastline. From that the Government derives a capping limit which it imposes on local authorities, effectively redistributing the business wealth created by industries operating within particular communities.

When this system was introduced in 1991, its effect was to favour local authorities in London and the South-East, at the expense of some of the declining towns and cities in the North, which suffered a net loss of income – and continue to do so. The west Cumbria area, administered by Copeland,

Allerdale and Cumbria County Council, has been suffering a net loss of income of over £750,000 a year ever since.

A sense of grievance over the way the area around Sellafield has been treated by the Government extends to the perceived lack of support it was given by Whitehall when it tried to gain assistance for economic regeneration from the EU. Working together during the late 1980s, the West Cumbria Development Fund (which BNFL largely finances), the local authorities, Copeland and Allerdale, and Jack Cunningham persuaded Bruce Millan, who was then responsible for this aspect of community policy, that the area needed and deserved assistance. They persuaded the commissioner to visit the area and he went away convinced by their case.

But EU support could be obtained only if the Government cooperated in what was intended to be a tripartite relationship involving local government, central Government and the EU. The UK Government took its time over helping west Cumbria obtain the Objective Two status, along with funding, which the EU was willing to provide.

One of the first problems the local authorities had to overcome was the condition that the European grants on offer could be made available only after the expenditure had been incurred. They also had to show that without the European grant the work being contemplated would not happen. It could not be used simply to replace central UK Government funding, for example. All of this involved cooperation between the local authorities and the Government, but despite the involvement of Lord Whitelaw, always a staunch supporter of his beloved Cumbria, the mills of the Department of the Environment ground exceeding slow.

One practical issue was that if European grant-aided work was carried out by the west Cumbrian local authorities, it was likely to be two or three months before the EU funds supporting it would arrive, and the local authorities had to find ways of bridging the gap. They themselves did not have borrowing powers to cover the few months' lag and were not allowed by the Government to obtain loans, despite the certainty of repayment – a self-evident nonsense. (This has now changed and local authority spending on European grant schemes can receive 100 per cent credit cover from the Government.)

It took those of us involved nearly two years to find a way through the bureaucracy, obfuscation and plain pig-headedness displayed by the Department of the Environment – not by the EU, which in my experience dealt with matters promptly. The Department gave the impression that it did not take kindly to local authorities, state-owned industries and opposition MPs combining to go direct to the EU for assistance. Eventually, however, although it did not put up any supporting funds directly, the Department agreed that the West Cumbria Development Fund and, later, the Rural Development Commission – both largely funded from within the public sector – could join the two local authorities in order to meet the requirement that EU funding had to be matched by the recipient country.

In 1990 the long-promised support from the EU finally got through. Both the Whitehaven and Workington Travel to Work areas were recognized by the EU and the Government as an Objective Two region eligible for EU structural funds. Some £11 million was provided for the development of two business parks, environmental initiatives, business support measures and attempts to stimulate tourism.

Now there appears to be a possibility of more EU funding reaching this Continental backwater, much of it to be spent on Westlakes. The Research Institute section of the planned expansion there is intended to create a scientific establishment which will build on Sellafield's experience of cleaning up its own environmental act, delivering solutions to environmental contamination problems within the international arena and exploiting them commercially.

The institute will concentrate on three main areas of activity: it will seek to establish greater understanding of how the environment is contaminated; develop ways of dealing with contamination; and in the longer-term try to develop ways of ensuring that industry does not contaminate the environment in the first place. These activities will be strengthened by the development of a parallel understanding of applied policy networks, such as Government and industry communications and environmental values.

All of this may sound like so much pie in the sky, but I have been to Westlakes and listened to the enthusiasts running the project. As a previous cynic, I came back convinced that there is a real chance of success. Whether the Westlakes Research Institute will be able to meet the target it has set itself of creating 1,400 jobs by the end of the century is open to question, but there is no doubt whatever that those jobs are going to be needed. A large part of the workforce at Sellafield, which has led the drive for improved pay and employment conditions within BNFL since the formation of the company, are going to find themselves looking for help from somewhere very soon.

Chapter Nine

Human Resources:

The Politics of Envy at Work

Sellafield is part of a state-owned company. As such, its employment conditions are dictated by what the Treasury happens to be thinking about inflationary wage pressures at that particular time, despite the pretence that the BNFL board is free to set all but the directors' salaries. The fact is that Government interference in the bargaining process, together with weak management at times, has created anomalies and distortions which are still being worked out of BNFL's pay and conditions system decades after they were introduced. This is especially true of Sellafield, which has been the major influence on that system.

Until now, Sellafield has been a difficult site to manage, the scene of constant change as impressive new plants have joined the venerable facilities inherited from the past. To get to work, employees have had to pick their way through a permanent building site, littered with the materials and debris of construction. It is hardly surprising, with so much happening, that on several occasions while I was with BNFL, the board expressed concern that the site was becoming unmanageable. Potential labour relations problems were bought off in order to make some sort of progress – but not overtly, because of the Treasury's exaggerated interest in the effect public sector settlements have on general pay levels in the UK.

All this is set to change. The major construction programme at Sellafield has been completed with the commissioning of THORP and there is nothing of a similar scale on the horizon – or likely to be. The management can therefore concentrate on operating the old and new plants more efficiently. The current Chairman, John Guinness – a Guinness from both the banking and brewing sides of the dynasty, as he is fond of telling anyone taking an interest in his surname – is determined that they should do so. This is a laudable objective, one which is clearly necessary if the nuclear power industry's competitiveness is to improve, and ultimately that must be in the interests of the Sellafield workforce itself.

Whether they will see it that way is another matter. Because of the continuous expansion which has taken place at Sellafield, the workforce has felt itself to be immune from the employment pressures felt elsewhere in the BNFL group, particularly at the enrichment factory at Capenhurst, on the Wirral, which has always operated in a highly competitive market area. Because of this sense of immunity, the Sellafield employee representatives have invariably led the charge for improved pay and conditions during BNFL's annual pay round negotiations – and sometimes in between them.

Sellafield's shop stewards learned early on that the very name Sellafield was enough to strike terror into the hearts of Government ministers and the BNFL board if they threatened to withdraw their members' labour. It is not only that the reprocessing of Magnox fuel has to be near continuous, because the fuel deteriorates quickly, leaching out radioactive materials; the management is also aware that production at the site can be brought to a standstill by a handful of employees, whether they are manual workers or members of the staff.

There have been several demonstrations of this over the years. The first came in February 1977, when a group of thirty-two changing-room attendants went on strike for more pay. The timing of the strike and the workers used to further a general push for higher wages for manual workers employed at Sellafield was opportunistic in the extreme. BNFL, still sensitive about being called the nuclear dustbin of the world, was preparing for the THORP public inquiry. The last thing it needed was the distraction of a major labour relations confrontation – and the workers knew it.

Employees in the active areas at Sellafield, where radioactive materials are handled, have to go through the changing rooms and put on protective clothing before they start work. They then have to change back into their ordinary clothing when they go off on their meal breaks (and tea breaks before they were bought out) and back again before resuming work. Finally they have to change to go home. At each stage, the attendants have to see that the radiation workers follow procedures designed to ensure that no radioactive materials leave the active areas on the workers' shoes or clothing. There have been stories of workers carrying radioactive materials into their homes because they have not followed the clean-up procedures correctly and of others climbing over barriers containing monitoring equipment in order to get off the site quickly. The equipment has now been changed to prevent this, but in the 1970s some sort of double check was necessary.

The initial strike by the thirty-two changing-room attendants led very quickly to another 3,000 manual workers being sent home. At first they continued to be paid, but their wages were stopped when they refused to cross the changing room barriers, manned by managers in the absence of attendants. The 3,000 were told that they were effectively on strike. The picket lines grew and the strikers began to get more desperate and belligerent as the weeks dragged on. Pickets began to block supplies of gases said by the management to be needed to ensure the safe operation of the plant.

At BNFL's headquarters at Risley we could believe only what we were told by the Sellafield management and the directors began to draw up contingency plans to deal with the crisis, including the possible use of troops to escort gas tankers through the Sellafield gates or even the use of helicopters to carry supplies in over the heads of the pickets. Department of Energy officials were briefed on the developing situation and eventually informed Tony Benn, the Secretary of State. Bernard Ingham, then Mr Benn's Director of Information, telephoned me on Friday 11 March 1977, as the strike entered its sixth week, to tell me that his boss was about to leave London for Sellafield, accompanied by an entourage which included his Principal Private Secretary, Brian Sedgemoor, MP, and Frances Morrell, one of his political advisers, neither of them supporters of nuclear power or of Sellafield.

Bernard sounded incredulous and I could not believe my ears either. It was unheard of for a Government minister to intervene in an industrial dispute directly. I immediately alerted Con Allday and we travelled up to Sellafield together in the company Jaguar. In the car Con told me that he suspected the gas supply situation at Sellafield was not as desperate as the site had made out and that everyone was over-reacting. When a proper audit was carried out later, he was shown to be right. There were sufficient supplies of safety gases to have kept the site going for several more weeks.

At a heated meeting in a Whitehaven hotel, Tony Benn told Con Allday that he must get the strike ended immediately. He would have become more involved in the negotiations himself, but Bernard Ingham reminded him that the Government had a prices and incomes policy and he would be very unpopular with his Cabinet colleagues if he was seen to be a party to any agreement which could be said to have breached the Government's own pay guidelines. The Benn party left, leaving Con Allday and the trade unions to pick up the pieces.

The unions seemed as bemused by the Secretary of State's appearance as Con and I were, although they must have thought that having dragged a Government minister up to Cumbria by specially chartered aircraft they had the company and its shareholder on the run.

They were also growing concerned, however, about the effect their apparent threat to safety appeared to have had on Tony Benn and his advisers and a few I spoke to seemed a little shamefaced about it. Overnight a settlement was reached. It gave the strikers from the changing rooms an extra £1 a week on their 'hazardous working allowance' – not much in today's currency or even then and £7 to £11 less than they had claimed. All of those involved, including the 3,000 workers who claimed to have been laid off following the initial dispute and not on strike, were given £120 each as a lump sum. I know that Con Allday felt pleased that the strike had been settled quickly, as Tony Benn wanted. He also thought that he had done a reasonable deal in the circumstances. Early the following week Con received a telling-off from the Secretary of State for breaching the Government's pay policy.

This was not the end of the matter, however. At the THORP public inquiry later that year, a former Sellafield employee, a Mr W. C. Robertson, suggested that the changing-room dispute had shown that industrial action could threaten the safety of the public. The Sellafield workforce should therefore give up the right to strike. In return they should be given terms and conditions of employment guaranteed to be equal to the best in equivalent posts in industry generally. Any disputes should be dealt with by arbitration and the arbitration award should be binding, Mr Robertson said.

BNFL and the trade unions regarded this as unnecessary, but acknowledged that they should negotiate agreed procedures to ensure that situations like the one that had occurred at the beginning of the year did not recur. The inquiry inspector, Mr Justice Parker, accepted this. He also said that picketing in aid of a strike should not be allowed to prevent the delivery of essential supplies. Nor should pickets prevent the attendance without hindrance of a small safety force to maintain surveillance and to take any necessary remedial action in the event of such things as the failure of water or electricity supplies. After the inquiry BNFL and the trade unions reached an agreement on safety cover and it has held – just.

The 1977 pay strike was settled by an increase in the 'hazardous working allowance' received by those on strike, not in general pay rates. Special allowances of one kind or another were often used at Sellafield and at the other BNFL factories as a device to circumvent pay restrictions imposed in the public sector, not just at BNFL.

I was involved in personnel matters throughout my career with BNFL and for some years had board-level responsibility for the function. During that time I cannot remember a single year in which the company was allowed to conduct its pay negotiations without interference. Detailed instructions were always sent from civil servants acting on behalf of the sponsoring Government department and the Treasury. At the same time we were invariably told that we must not say so to the unions.

In case it is thought that only Labour governments intervene during public sector pay negotiations I had better make it clear that in my experience Conservative ministers get involved in much the same way as Tony Benn did. During the miners' strike in 1982 Con Allday met Giles Shaw (later Lord Shaw), who was then Minister of Energy, and was told to get BNFL's pay negotiations settled as quickly as possible, as it was essential that nuclear power supplies were maintained – a sensible position for the minister to take. But the unions were also aware of the pressure BNFL would be under to reach a swift settlement and held out. In the end Con could get the settlement needed by the Government only by allowing the company negotiators to settle at the figure specified by the Treasury, which was not acceptable to the unions, but over an eleven-month rather than a twelve-month period. Later, of course, Con received another ministerial rocket.

I felt sorry for Tony Mills, the Personnel Director who had the unenviable task of leading the management team at most of the pay negotiations. Sometimes he was given his instructions by the civil servants only minutes before going into a meeting and then had to pretend that he was a free agent – fooling nobody. As a journalist I had always suspected that the Government – of whatever complexion – interfered too much in the affairs of state-owned industry, but the extent of its meddling amazed me.

All the Department of Energy (later the Department of Trade and Industry) and the Treasury were interested in was BNFL negotiating a percentage pay settlement which was sufficiently low for the Government to be able to claim that it had the state-owned sector of industry under control, which it could then use as a stick to beat other industries following behind in the pay queue. Neither the Department nor the Treasury appeared to care very much about the deals made around the edges of the central settlement figure, dismissing them as marginal improvements in conditions. But the cost of an extra day's holiday here or a new 'special allowance' there added up to substantial additions to the pay bill and were often the only way we could implement the Government-imposed wage deals.

The peripheral deals made during the annual pay round or, in the case of Sellafield in particular, by local management and trade unions at other times of the year when pressures built up led to very complicated pay structures. When the company moved to computerize its payroll in the early 1980s, the first programme which was written could not accommodate all the variables. More often than not the central Personnel Directorate heard of these site deals only after the event.

The 'hazardous working conditions' allowance used for settling the 1977 pay dispute at Sellafield was one of dozens of special allowances which were permitted to proliferate, many of them relating to working conditions in particular buildings on the site. But none of these extra allowances had as much impact on general pay levels at Sellafield as the tea-break agreement, which had been allowed to become the accepted practice by the mid-1970s.

With two tea breaks, as well as meal breaks, employees in the radiation areas at Sellafield were effectively working little more than three hours a day. The rest of the time was spent eating, drinking, smoking (forbidden in the active areas) or reading the newspapers and getting in and out of working clothes and the changing rooms through the radiation-detection monitoring devices. Because of the limited time available for work, extensive overtime was the norm. It is small wonder that Sellafield was known locally as the holiday camp.

The tea-break farce went on for over a decade, although desultory attempts were occasionally made to bring it to an end. Eventually it was negotiated out of the system by Alan Johnson, the Executive Director rushed up to Sellafield to take over responsibility for the site in 1988 when Gordon Steele, the Site Director, was forced to retire early by ill-health. Alan did a deal which provided the workforce with a cash sum of £1,000 each and an extra £6 a week (rising to £7) for all time. The deal cost the company an immediate £4.5 million or more and was a continuing addition to the Sellafield wages bill of at least £1.5 million a year – and yet it was reckoned to be money well spent. It enabled BNFL to man up THORP and other new plants on a more efficient basis from the start.

Alan Johnson tried to instil a sense of realism into the Sellafield workforce through regular briefing sessions and the preparation of a video, shown to all the site's employees, which warned them that if costs were not brought under better control, THORP would lose its contracts with its UK and overseas customers. Unfortunately, copies of this video reached the television companies and were used to fan speculation that the THORP order book was under threat – speculation which we now know was correct, although we tried to play the risk down at the time.

There was another example in 1989 of how deals made around the edges of pay negotiations can lead to a greater cost burden than the basic agreement. This pay round was apparently settled at a level of 5 per cent, satisfying the civil servants of the Treasury and the Department of Energy and presumably their ministers. But to get the trade unions to accept this figure Tony Mills, with the explicit agreement of Neville Chamberlain, had to agree that the company would begin talks on the issue of reducing the working week to thirty-five hours – a TUC target which every trade union negotiator wanted to be the first to reach.

At that time the fixed working week in BNFL was thirty-seven hours and it was obvious that without concessions from the unions a two-hour reduction would cost a great deal of money. The national trade unions officers involved in the pay talks saw a real opportunity of making a breakthrough which they could use as a lever elsewhere in the nuclear industry and other manufacturing sectors and took up the offer of talks approved by Neville Chamberlain. In my opinion the pass was sold the moment Neville, who was up against the stops imposed by the Treasury, agreed that talks could start on the thirty-five hour week, even though he stipulated that any new arrangements could be introduced only if they were self-financing.

A joint working group of management and trade union representatives was established immediately after the 1989 pay negotiations were completed. The group's task was to study the cost implications of the shorter working week (a description which Mr Chamberlain preferred to the four-and-a-half-day week or nine-day fortnight which others called it) and to make recommendations. All of the factories and head office were represented on this group, which was chaired by Pat

Upson, who was then Director of Enrichment Division, with the expressed purpose of injecting line-management experience into the exercise.

Discussions dragged on for nearly a year, but eventually Pat brought a paper to the Personnel Committee, which I chaired as the responsible board member. The paper argued that looking at the company as a whole, the thirty-five hour week could be brought in at nil extra cost, because of concessions over working practices which the trade unions were willing to make.

I refused to accept this recommendation immediately and sent the paper back for more work to be done on it. Instinctively, I could not believe that the working week could be shortened and the same amount of work be done in the reduced time available. But I had never managed a factory or any manual workers and the management side of the working party chaired by Pat Upson was entirely made up of people with hands-on labour relations and managerial experience. The group included John Hall, one of the senior managers at Sellafield, although it was usually Grahame Smith, the head of the Sellafield site, or his deputy, Peter Manning, who attended the Personnel Committee meetings.

When the paper came back to the Personnel Committee I bounced it once again and once more Pat Upson took it away. By now he was getting irritated with me, and I cannot blame him. I was obviously playing for time, still suspicious that there was something wrong about the no-cost equation which the paper purported to prove, even though I was unable to fault the figures as they were presented. The trade unions became increasingly tetchy too. They had accepted the terms of the joint report months earlier. I had several conversations with Neville Chamberlain and he told me that as long as the agreement was truly self-financing it could go ahead.

The next time the joint proposals came to the Personnel Committee I went round the table asking the representatives of each of the factories and of head office to confirm that they accepted the paper's central conclusion that the shorter working week would not add to company costs and that they stood by the individual inputs from their sites on which this conclusion was based. I put them on the spot quite deliberately because of my own doubts. Every site representative – including Sellafield – gave me the assurance I was seeking and on this basis I reluctantly agreed that the joint report recommendations could be implemented. As I had anticipated, the introduction of the thirty-five hour week at BNFL made headline news and the Government was not very pleased.

Less than a month after the deal I met Grahame Smith at one of BNFL's regular Senior Management Group conferences. We were having a drink at the bar before the conference dinner and began to discuss the shorter working week agreement. Grahame informed me that I was naïve if I really thought the deal would be self-financing. The true cost was still being worked out, he said, but it was obvious that the new arrangement was going to cost Sellafield several millions of pounds a year in extra wages. Within Pat Upson's working group the Sellafield representative had said that the agreement's effect would be neutral as far as his site was concerned.

I asked Grahame Smith to explain why Sellafield had gone along with the proposition that the new deal would be self-financing. 'Well, it's what Neville Chamberlain wanted, isn't it?' he replied. The reasoning of his representative on the joint working group, John Hall, was more complicated than that, I suspect. He must have felt under considerable peer pressure not to stand out against a deal which all the other site management and trade union representatives on the working group said was feasible. As our conversation grew more heated, attracting the attention of others, I called Neville Chamberlain over and told him what Grahame Smith had just told me. I left the two of them arguing at the bar.

The BNFL board had to be told about the extra costs which Sellafield now said the company would have to face and this task fell to Neville Chamberlain. Somehow, in the telling of what had happened I found that I was taking most of the blame, as board member responsible for personnel. My mistake, if there was one, was to believe what I was told by colleagues, a congenital failing much in evidence at the end of my career with BNFL. Interestingly, however, the workforce at Sellafield seemed to know who they had to thank for the shorter working week. They called their extra days off 'Nev days'.

In the light of what had gone on within Pat Upson's working group I wanted the BNFL board to tell Grahame Smith that he was stuck with the deal made on his behalf and he would have to find the cost savings needed to pay for the site's error from elsewhere in the site budget. If that happened, I saw no sign of it.

While the shorter working week débâcle was not cited as the reason for it, changes were made soon afterwards in the personnel function. Tony Mills, who was not even on the Pat Upson working party, was transferred to a new post as Director of BNFL Enterprise Limited, a company established to coordinate all of the BNFL group's investment in local communities, a role which had long interested him and which he fills extremely well.

I helped to recruit Tony's successor, Alan Hanslip, and was then told that he would report directly to Neville Chamberlain and that I would no longer be responsible for personnel. The Personnel Directorate was renamed Human Resources – a title I dislike intensely. It smacks of people being seen in much the same light as pound notes, parcels of land and machinery, something to be used.

So great has Sellafield's influence been on BNFL that in 1988 Neville Chamberlain seriously contemplated breaking the company up for pay negotiation purposes and moving to site bargaining, with no central involvement. This would really have put the general managers of Capenhurst, Springfields and Chapelcross on their mettle. They had long complained that Sellafield was leading them by the nose and they were being forced to pay rates which their businesses could not afford. They claimed that they would be able to get away with paying far lower rates if they were on their own, or even – in the case of Capenhurst – that a moratorium on pay rises would be acceptable for a few years. It was an easy thing to say when there was no chance of it happening, more worrying when there was a prospect of the site general managers being given the freedom they said they wanted.

The main argument against site bargaining was that pay rates at Sellafield would be even higher if the shop stewards there were left to negotiate with their local management freely, without the checks and balances provided by shop stewards from the other sites, who recognized the dangers to employment of excessive wage increases. In the end the idea of site bargaining was quietly dropped when the national trade union officers informed Neville Chamberlain that if this happened, the individual factory units would not be large enough to justify them getting involved in the annual pay round or any other key discussions. The thought of the Sellafield shop stewards, in particular, acting without the leavening of realism provided by the national trade union officers was too much for BNFL to contemplate.

Instead, in December 1988 BNFL negotiated what was known as a facilitating agreement with its industrial trade unions, which enabled fundamental changes in working practices to be negotiated by the company's divisions. The deal was that any savings arising from these changes would be split on a three-way basis: a third of the savings going to the company, a third to customers through price reductions (at least in theory) and a third to the employees concerned. It was seen as a very important agreement at the time, but I am not sure how well it worked in practice. It seemed to have withered on the vine long before I left BNFL.

It was not only relationships with the industrial trade unions which were complicated by Government interference. Negotiations with the staff unions were equally fraught. When

BNFL was formed in 1971 its personnel practices were those of the Civil Service, from which it had emerged via the UKAEA. The company's pay and conditions links with the Civil Service were not broken until 1979, opening the way for the development of a more industrially based and flexible staff and grading structure. But the unions representing BNFL staff still represented people employed in the Civil Service. The national officers of the unions were therefore always looking over their shoulder at what use they could make across the boundaries of agreements concluded at BNFL or, occasionally, within the Civil Service.

Many of the senior managers at Sellafield and elsewhere in the BNFL group are themselves members of the former Civil Service trade unions. Until 1981 there were only about thirty people employed by BNFL who were not covered by collective bargaining agreements and even today there are no more than 200 people who do not have their pay negotiated for them by the trade unions. It is perfectly normal to have some representatives of the two sides at the negotiating table belonging to the same trade union, which is hardly designed to reinforce management resolve.

The tensions this creates were demonstrated during a strike by non-industrial members of staff during the 1989 pay round, which was conducted separately from the industrial workforce negotiations. This strike was again centred on Sellafield and this time it was the turn of the staff unions to demonstrate that they could halt production just as effectively as the industrial unions if they wanted to. They withdrew the labour of a small number of people at the Calder Hall power station, which provides essential steam and electricity supplies to the Sellafield site.

Senior managers succeeded in maintaining the back-up systems to ensure safety on the site, using portable oil-fired generators, but reprocessing was halted. Some of the senior managers who went into work slept at the site on camp beds for several days while the strike lasted. This showed considerable dedication, since they stood to benefit if the strike succeeded and had a great deal of sympathy with their striking trade union colleagues.

Being at Sellafield, this dispute also excited ministers. Christopher Harding and I were called in to reassure the then Minister for Energy, Peter Morrison, that everything was under control. At least, I think that was what the meeting was about – my abiding memory is of the minister showing us how the dozens of clockwork toys which he kept on the meeting table in his office worked and telling us the names he had given to them.

It was not only senior managers who were caught up in the dilemma of whether it was right for them, as people involved in the pay-bargaining process on behalf of management, to remain trade union members. When I joined BNFL several of the directors of the company were members of the Institution of Professional Civil Servants, the principal staff union within BNFL. The General Secretary of that union had just taken up the cudgels on their behalf with Tony Benn. He won them substantial pay increases, mitigating the worst effects of the anomalies created by the Government controlling directors' salaries rather more successfully than the directors managed to control general pay rates in the company. The sorry state of affairs which this produced as far as pay differentials was concerned is clearly shown in BNFL's annual reports of that time. It is the other side of the coin from the one we are now seeing as the salaries of the directors of the newly privatized companies are jacked up ever higher.

The distortion in pay differentials was at its worst in the mid-1970s. The 1975–6 annual report – covering the year I joined BNFL – shows that two of the executive directors of the company were paid in the salary range of £10,000 to £12,500. Another seventy-seven employees who were not board members were paid in the same range. One director was paid in the range £12,500 to £15,000 – the same as twenty-two employees. Only one director, Con Allday, the

Chief Executive, received more than non-board members: he was paid £15,355 that year.

The overlap in the salaries of directors and some of the senior managers reporting to them caused by Treasury control of board members' salaries persisted right through to the mid-1980s, when Christopher Harding arrived from the private sector and set out to create a pay structure which gave more recognition to the contribution made to BNFL's progress by its directors. As one of those directors, I am personally grateful for what he did for me. It has to be said, however, that he had only partial success and that such success as he did have led to different distortions, which are still there to some extent.

The first problem Christopher Harding had to address was that the Chief Executive he had chosen, Neville Chamberlain, was not a main board director when the choice was made. He was appointed to the board and made Chief Executive within the space of two months. The salary awarded to him for the responsibilities of his new post by the Government was lower than that of his board colleagues – an obvious nonsense. I provided Christopher Harding with his first opportunity to do something about Neville Chamberlain's situation.

Almost as soon as Christopher Harding became Chairman and while BNFL was deep in the throes of the nuclear industry's post-Chernobyl crisis, I was offered the post of Director of Corporate Affairs at Eurotunnel by Lord Pennock, who was then its Chairman. Eurotunnel was going through a bad patch at the time and there was a lot of newspaper speculation about who might be called in to improve its image. Christopher Harding did not want me to leave BNFL and, rather to my surprise, negotiated a pay rise for me which was substantial by public-sector standards, although still not as good as the offer from Eurotunnel. He also secured improvements in my pension provisions, which I am finding very useful now.

It would be nice to feel that Christopher Harding battled so skilfully to keep me at BNFL because he regarded me as an important member of his new team. But as he immediately used my salary increase as a way of improving Neville Chamberlain's situation, he seems to have had mixed motives. He did the same thing a few years later, when I was bought off a possible move to Pilkingtons. Briefly, until the Bolter lever was used to lift Neville Chamberlain's salary, I was the highest-paid director of BNFL, apart from Christopher Harding himself – flattering, but totally unrealistic and unfair to Neville and to some of my older board colleagues. The trade unions were aware of these anomalies – indeed, they referred wryly to my salary position during one of the annual pay negotiations.

However, Government policy ensured that I went from being the highest-paid executive director of BNFL to the lowest-paid in the space of four years. When he was Secretary of State for Energy, Cecil Parkinson was honest enough to set out in writing the Government's philosophy on boardroom salaries in the public sector. Lord Parkinson told Christopher Harding that the salary of BNFL's directors would only be increased if this was necessary to retain the services of younger directors who might otherwise leave the company or if it was necessary in order to recruit good people. Not a word about loyalty or performance.

The use which Christopher Harding made of my job offers to help Neville Chamberlain is not well known, but he talked openly to many people about how he used the opportunity provided by John Hayles's retirement as Finance Director of BNFL. He went outside the company for John's successor and recruited Peter Phillips at a salary of around £120,000 a year, almost exactly double the salary of the man he succeeded. Alan Johnson, Bill Wilkinson and I – the three remaining executive directors – were told by Christopher Harding that he intended to use the salary awarded to Mr Phillips to get Neville Chamberlain's salary raised again – and promptly did so. At the same time we were told that nothing could be done for us and he would quite understand if we decided to move on.

So, during the financial year 1990–91, the extraordinary situation was created where one of the directors was paid three times as much as one of the others, effectively creating a two-tier board. The annual report shows that the salary ranges of the directors went from £50–55,000 a year to £155–160,000. As soon as they could, Alan and Bill negotiated early retirements. At the age of fifty-three I was too young to do so, but I was extremely disillusioned and immediately shot copies of my curriculum vitae off to over a dozen executive search companies and hoped for the best.

It was not a good time in the jobs market, however – or maybe, as the Cecil Parkinson note suggested, I was losing my attraction with age – and nothing came of my attempt to get away from BNFL. In 1993 I received a CBE in the Birthday Honours List and was told how much I was needed by the company. With something of a sigh, I decided to stay with BNFL through to my retirement. I hope the award was in recognition of the contribution which I had made to the nuclear industry, as the citation said, but I know that the Honours List is also used in lieu of salary increases by the Civil Service and I suspect that this was part of the motivation.

I have taken time to describe some of the turmoil which has affected salaries at the top of the company because I believe that it had an effect on the attitudes not only of the people directly concerned but throughout BNFL. Leads are set from the top and there is a preoccupation with salaries and status in state-owned companies which is probably not found to the same extent in the private sector – except when people from the state-owned industries move over.

Latterly the directors who remain in the public sector have seen the salaries of their former colleagues whose businesses have been privatized – gas, steel, electricity, the water authorities – shoot ahead of the ones they received from the state for doing much the same job. Those left behind would not be human if they do not feel envious when they see their former colleagues getting ten times as much as them in salaries and bonuses, becoming instant millionaires. Indeed, despite their jibes about Labour MPs indulging in the politics of envy when they complain about exorbitant directors' salaries in the newly privatized industries, I have heard quite a few Tory MPs and ministers make envious noises themselves, even about the much lower salaries paid to the directors of companies like BNFL.

It is arguable whether the directors of the newly privatized companies are paid too much. Personally, I think they have been greedy and insensitive. As they are still running monopolies or near-monopolies it is doubtful if they are worth the salaries paid in companies operating in more competitive environments. But then, they were often grossly underpaid when the state acted as their shareholders, and nobody seemed to get excited about that.

Most of those who have moved across to the private sector have had no trouble in making the transition. They have proved themselves to be the same able people as they always were. When the former leaders of state-owned companies have entered what Tory politicians like to think of as the more disciplined, market-driven arena of the private sector, most of them have revelled in the greater freedom they have had to run their businesses, freed from the dead hand of the Treasury and the sponsoring Government departments.

Maybe that alone is sufficient argument for privatizing nuclear power. But for reasons I will explain, I do not believe that such a privatization exercise should ever include BNFL, certainly not while it owns and operates Sellafield.

Chapter Ten

Privatization:

A Pause For Clause Four

In the summer of 1996 the Government will sell off eight nuclear power stations for around what it cost to build just one of them, the £2,750 million Sizewell B PWR station, commissioned only last year. Anyone offered an 'eight for the price of one' bargain in a car boot sale would be looking for hidden snags and potential investors in British Energy Limited (BEL) should exercise similar caution before they buy into the nuclear power business.

The price which the Government expects to get for the seven AGR stations and one PWR which Nuclear Electric and Scottish Nuclear are to take into BEL is an indication of how desperate it is to get as much of the nuclear industry off its hands as possible. This is not so much a case of the Government selling off the family silver as it disposing of a canteen of old and unwanted cutlery for the best price it can obtain.

To get even this far, it has had to retain a hefty slice of the industry in state ownership, using BNFL as a nuclear black holes corporation into which it can dump the reprocessing, decommissioning and waste management costs associated with the old Magnox power stations. The sale of what remains still does not look particularly attractive, however, and the Government may have to go the extra distance to get the City interested in this bargain basement sale.

The Department of Trade and Industry did nothing to increase the value of the reactors it intends to sell when it announced the AGR and PWR privatization in its 1995 White Paper on the future structure of the nuclear industry. There was a lot of *caveat emptor* tucked away in that document. Michael Heseltine, then President of the Board of Trade, refused to be swayed by any of the usual arguments put forward in support of the nuclear industry's case for further state assistance and was extremely gloomy about the industry's prospects, certainly in the short term.

Despite special pleading that it would reduce the amount of carbon dioxide emitted by fossil fuel stations, conserve oil and gas, boost employment and the economy and help retain nuclear expertise in the UK, Mr Heseltine declined to provide the subsidy of at least £1,000 million towards the £3,500 million cost of building another PWR at Sizewell which the nuclear industry was seeking.

Worse than that, Mr Heseltine said that he did not believe that private finance for a new nuclear station was likely to be forthcoming either, without the transfer of specific nuclear risks away from private investors.

When it heard that the Government's forty-year-old obsession with nuclear power was over and that the industry was on its own, Nuclear Electric said that it would explore the possibility of attracting private sector finance for a new station without Government underwriting or subsidies. Wiser counsels prevailed, however, and the embryo BEL organization announced in December last year that it was not going ahead with plans to build Sizewell C in Suffolk and Hinkley C in Somerset because they would not have been commercial. Plans for a third PWR which were current at the time of the electricity supply industry (ESI) privatization in 1989 had already been dropped.

The BEL announcement was almost certainly prompted by the Government. Given past experience it was an essential part of the build-up to the privatization of Sizewell B and the seven AGRs, which are now operating as well as any nuclear power stations in the world, even if they are being given away by the Government as a make weight.

In 1989 the Department of Energy, now absorbed within the DTI, was forced to withdraw nuclear power from the ESI privatization at the last moment because potential investors were concerned about a number of uncertainties relating to the cost and efficiency of nuclear electricity generation, one of the most important being the cost of financing the three new PWR stations then planned in addition to Sizewell B.

Another area of uncertainty which investors found off-putting seven years ago was the potential for significantly increased costs associated with the 'back end' of the nuclear fuel cycle – spent fuel reprocessing, radioactive waste management and disposal and the decommissioning of nuclear plants.

The Government has addressed part of this problem by announcing that it will keep all eleven of the old Magnox power stations in public ownership, using BNFL as a vehicle for the purpose. Six of the stations are currently owned and operated by Nuclear Electric, while three are being decommissioned. The other two, Calder Hall at Sellafield and Chapelcross in Scotland, already belong to BNFL.

By transferring responsibility for Nuclear Electric and Scottish Nuclear's Magnox stations to BNFL, the Government has given the company an incentive to keep the stations running for as long as there is a market for the electricity they produce and to get Magnox fuel and reprocessing costs down. BNFL has been turned into its own customer for these services.

Somewhat optimistically, the Government has estimated that the decommissioning and waste management liabilities associated with the closure of the former NE and SN Magnox stations can be financed by an £8,500 million fund earning 3.5 per cent a year. As only £5,900 million will have been raised by the time the AGR and PWR stations are handed over to BEL, even on its own figures the Government will have to fill the gap with £2,600 million of the £3,000 million or so it hopes to get from the NE and SN privatization.

Surprisingly, in the circumstances, the Government will abolish the 10 per cent 'nuclear levy' on consumer electricity bills this year. This has been imposed since 1990 to help cover the costs of decommissioning and had been expected to remain in place until at least 1998. Removing the levy is expected to lead to a fall of up to eight per cent in electricity prices, providing a saving for domestic customers of at least £20 a year, a privatization sweetener useful in the run-up to a general election. In order to do this and still balance the books when it transfers the NE and SN Magnox stations over to BNFL the Government will be indulging in some rather dubious sleight of hand at the expense of future generations of taxpayers.

Nuclear Electric and Scottish Nuclear have always estimated their liability for decommissioning and Magnox wastes at £9,800 million, rather than the £8,500 million the Government is now talking about, having assumed a conventional discount rate of 2 per cent. By increasing the discount rate to 3.5 per cent for the first twenty-five years the Department of Trade and Industry has achieved an instant 'saving' of £1,300 million. That might just about be acceptable if the Government planned to set up a segregated fund to cover the cost of the Magnox liabilities, investing similar sums of money every year to meet the eventual costs, but it has no intention of doing so.

Without such a dedicated fund the correct figure to use is surely the undiscounted cost of £15,000 million which some future Government will have to cover when the day of reckoning comes for decommissioning and waste management at the end of the Magnox programme.

To get to its £8,500 million figure for discounted Magnox liabilities, the DTI has also plucked another rabbit out of the hat. It has assumed that BNFL will reduce costs by £500 million by adopting the so-called 'safestore' approach towards Magnox decommissioning, which postpones full site clearance to 135 years after reactor closure, compared to the previously expected 100 years. The problem with that assumption is that another arm of the Government, the Department of the Environment, has said that decommissioning should be undertaken as soon as it is reasonably practicable to do so.

In a review of radioactive waste management policy published in 1995, John Gummer, Secretary of State for the Environment, described the 'safestore' approach to decommissioning as only one of a number of potentially feasible and acceptable decommissioning strategies. He also warned that nuclear operators would be unwise to take steps which 'foreclose technically or economically the option of completing the decommissioning process on an earlier time-scale should that be required' – and who knows what future Governments and their electors will require.

Mr Gummer also announced that in order to ensure that decommissioning strategies remain soundly based as circumstances change, they will be reviewed every five years by the Health and Safety Executive, who will consult the Environment Agencies. That introduces a further element of uncertainty into the decommissioning cost equation, which has plenty of variables already with the more complex dismantling processes yet to be tackled by operators who are still gaining experience in an extremely difficult area of industrial expertise.

Decommissioning cost uncertainties apply with equal force to all nuclear power stations, whoever owns them. By contrast with the 'put off the evil day' approach which it is taking towards its own state-owned Magnox stations, however, the Government has decided to set up an independent trust to manage the segregated fund which will be established to cover the decommissioning of the privatized AGR and PWR stations. This trust will enter into a contract with BEL under which it will receive funds, invest them and make payments from the invested funds to meet long term decommissioning costs, thus ensuring that these liabilities do not fall to the taxpayer by default, as Magnox costs will.

The next area of uncertainty facing the new owners of BEL is the cost of reprocessing – or its alternative – despite the THORP reprocessing contracts signed with BNFL NE and SN a bare six weeks before the two state-owned generating companies heard that the AGR and PWR parts of their businesses were to be privatized.

Tim Eggar, the minister responsible for Energy at the DTI, has argued that the signing of those fixed-price contracts removed one of the barriers to privatization. I am not so sure it is as easy as that. Like the dog which did not bark, it is necessary to be aware of what did not happen when the THORP reprocessing deals were signed in March 1995. Under these contracts NE's successor company BEL will only be committed to having half of its AGR spent fuel reprocessed in THORP, some 3,600 tonnes over twenty years. The rest will be stored, pending a decision about what to do with it some time in the future.

SN will take into the newly privatized business a similarly half-hearted commitment to THORP. It is down to have some 1,700 tonnes of AGR fuel reprocessed over twenty years and has talked BNFL into agreeing to have the remaining lifetime arisings of AGR fuel – an estimated 1,044 tonnes – sent to Sellafield, with no certainty over what will happen to it.

Meanwhile, BNFL is desperately trying to market reprocessing capacity for the second decade of THORP's operation overseas, having filled the plant's first ten years' capacity. As a result there are arguments developing over whether it should be allowed to separate out plutonium for such countries as South Korea.

The Government has recognized that when it floats BEL

in the summer of 1996 the market will be looking for as much certainty over the newly privatized company's future costs as possible. Having bitten the bullet and allowed THORP to start up, the Government should seize the opportunity to see that it is operated in the national interest, particularly now that it is to remain in the public sector.

Although SN, in particular, has argued that long-term storage of spent fuel, followed by direct disposal, would be cheaper than reprocessing and the disposal of waste only, this is disputed by BNFL and is far from certain. Nor has it been demonstrated that the people of west Cumbria or any other community will agree to having unreprocessed fuel dumped beneath them – and I have already shown what politicians do when faced with enough opposition. In my view, therefore, the Government should persuade BEL – before privatization takes place – to agree to have all of its AGR and PWR spent fuel reprocessed in THORP at fixed prices, taking another uncertainty out of the frame. The Government should also think again about the future organization, management and funding of radioactive waste disposal, another activity where uncertain costs worry potential investors. The present arrangement is an organizational nightmare.

Nirex – currently owned by Nuclear Electric, Scottish Nuclear, BNFL and the UKAEA – has responsibility for finding a disposal route for nearly all of the intermediate- and low-level waste stored in the UK but not for high-level waste. It is BNFL's job to safeguard the High Level Waste stored at Sellafield, but not to get rid of it. Nobody has yet been charged with that task. Any research into the disposal of HLW has long been the responsibility of the Department of the Environment. But geological studies into the disposal of HLW were discontinued by the department fifteen years ago and the best that it could manage in its recent policy review was an indication that it would 'shortly be initiating work on a research strategy for the disposal of HLW and spent fuel'.

To confuse matters further the main disposal facility for

LLW, the Drigg site near Sellafield, is owned and managed by BNFL, not Nirex – and the Department of the Environment now intends to examine a proposal that short-lived ILW should be buried there as well as LLW. It is time to resolve the uncertainties and make one organization responsible for the disposal of all forms of radioactive waste – and that organization should be wholly state-owned, in order to provide the long-term assurance on safety, stretching out over thousands of years, that the public wants.

Nirex could be that organization, but not with the newly privatized companies simply being integrated into the company's existing structure alongside state-owned BNFL, as currently planned. That arrangement relies on the Government continuing to exercise its influence through a golden share and agreement in principle by the private sector shareholders of Nirex to follow Government policy 'as set out from time to time' – another potential area of uncertainty for investors in BEL to consider.

It would be simpler to make Nirex a wholly-owned subsidiary of BNFL, which has had a predatory eye on Nirex for some time. It owns the Sellafield site which Nirex is investigating and is, of course, to remain in the public sector. Over half of the waste destined for the Nirex repository comes from BNFL's operations anyway. Because that might make BNFL too big and diffuse to manage, an early opportunity should be taken to sell off the front end of the company's business – uranium enrichment at Capenhurst on the Wirral, fuel manufacture at Springfields, near Preston, and contract engineering, once housed at BNFL's Risley headquarters site but now accommodated in Manchester.

BNFL will no doubt argue against this, on the grounds that it has to be able to provide a full nuclear fuel cycle service if it is to compete effectively overseas, an argument it has deployed with some success in the past. I have seen no evidence that this is so, however. When I was with the company we certainly tried to get UK and overseas customers interested in buying into a total package arrangement which would have linked a fuel supply service to reprocessing in a cradle-to-grave arrangement, but we never had any success. Selling off the front end business is in my view the only way of privatizing any part of BNFL, despite the Government's insistence that it has not ruled out selling the company off intact as a longer-term option. To my mind the company's nuclear black holes corporation role precludes that for all time.

A quarter of a century ago there were thought to be few obstacles to the early privatization of the newly formed BNFL. The company's role as a producer of nuclear weapons materials worried a few people and there was a dawning realization that the costs of waste management might be greater than had been anticipated, but neither of these problems seemed insurmountable. The real difficulty, which the City if not the Civil Service would have recognized if there had been an early attempt at privatization, was that the new company's contractual arrangements with its principal customers were either vague or unsuitable, certainly no foundation for a successful flotation.

Since it started to trade BNFL has invested hundreds of millions of pounds in new plants, mainly at Sellafield, on the strength of contracts which have had to be renegotiated subsequently or with no more security than a 'letter of comfort' from the Government. It has produced its accounts on the same basis – all in good faith, I hasten to add – and until spring 1995 most of its trade with its UK customers was still being conducted more on the basis of trust than anything else. This may have been allright when all of the companies involved were owned by the state but it would not have remained acceptable to its shareholders for very long if BNFL had been pitched into the competitive world of the private sector.

Those in the Labour Party who still hanker after the good old days of Clause Four should study the way in which the component parts of civil nuclear power have managed their trading relationships as an example of what actually happens when the state gets involved in business. The mess which was created is acknowledged in the Government White Paper and it is only the nuclear industry's desire to present itself as a credible target for privatization which has led to the contractual and organizational shambles described in the White Paper being tackled.

BNFL had been seen as an early target for at least partial privatization from day one of its existence. It is not only the Conservatives who saw the company in this light but the Labour Party as well. The Act establishing British Nuclear Fuels Limited (later to become a plc, but retaining the initials BNFL for logo purposes) was brought in by Edward Heath's Government immediately after his general election victory, but it had been drafted while the previous Labour Government was in power.

Although BNFL was formed out of parts of the UKAEA with the state owning all of the shares, the legislation brought in by Edward Heath, inherited from Labour, allowed up to 49 per cent of these shares to be sold off without further legislation. That is still the formal position today, although the option seems unlikely ever to be exercised.

When it was in opposition the Conservative Party was unwilling to support legislation which provided for a majority shareholding by the state and when they came into power the Tories considered privatizing BNFL totally. However, the incoming Heath Government was persuaded by Whitehall officials that for reasons of national security, associated with the production of plutonium and weapons materials, the Government must retain a majority shareholding. If that was true of BNFL then, it is difficult to see what has changed since, except that there is now even more plutonium to be kept secure at Sellafield.

Just how close the new company came to at least partial privatization can be gauged from the confident statement made by the company's first Chairman, Sir John Hill, at an inaugural press conference that he expected BNFL to set off on the privatization trail within six months. The Heath Government never corrected Sir John's indication that privatization was just around the corner and there appears to have been no public opposition to the idea, even from sections of the media which would now almost certainly campaign against releasing a plutonium-producing business from state control.

The thing which stopped an early sale of a large slice of BNFL in 1971 was a planned reorganization of the whole of the nuclear power industry, in which it was thought that the new company might play an important part. By then there were only two nuclear power station building consortia left out of the original five – and even those two were in trouble. They were the Nuclear Power Group (Reyrolle Parsons, Clarke Chapman-John Thompson, McAlpine) and British Nuclear Design and Construction (GEC, Babcock and Wilcox, Taylor Woodrow). Both were badly hit by a shortage of new power station orders and both had run into construction problems with the AGR power stations they were building.

One possibility was that the two groups might merge. Another, put forward by Sir John Hill, was that a bit of both of the consortia (the two big boilermakers, Clarke Chapman-John Thompson and Babcock and Wilcox) should merge with the newly-formed and state-owned BNFL. If that had happened, the privatization of BNFL – including Sellafield, with all of its national security implications – would have come in by the back door before the privatization of the electricity supply industry, with or without its nuclear power stations, was even talked about.

It took four years to reorganize the reactor side of the nuclear power industry. Out of the reorganization came the National Nuclear Corporation (NNC), which took over the design and construction activities of both consortia. There was no place in the new organization for BNFL after all, although the company did look at the possibility of merging with NNC itself in the late 1980s, largely as a means of escaping from state control. In the event, NNC has been as badly affected by a shortage of new nuclear power station orders as the companies it succeeded.

The possible privatization of BNFL was a talking point at most of the company's annual report press conferences and on one famous occasion Con Allday had the temerity to tell journalists that in his view BNFL was nearly ready to go to the market, after a run of excellent financial results. In an interview with the *Observer* in November 1984 Con speculated that BNFL was likely to be privatized 'within the next year to 18 months' and valued the company at £500 million.

Con suggested that the most suitable approach to privatization might be a two-stage placement. First there could be a 25 per cent offering to the institutions, which could be fully briefed on the nature of BNFL's business and its prospects. Then, if the first offering was successful, there could be a 24 per cent public flotation. Two of BNFL's merchant bankers, Samuel Montagu and Kleinwort Benson, had advised BNFL that it would be possible to go ahead on this two-stage basis. Con emphasized that in his view there was no question of more than 49 per cent of BNFL's shares being sold. 'This is because in the public mind we are dealing with something closely associated with weapons and public acceptability demands the Government remaining in ultimate control. A golden share, or something similar, would not be sufficient,' he said.

Far from being pleased with Con Allday's attempt to prepare the way for at least partial privatization, Peter Walker, then Secretary of State for Energy, sent him a pretty terse message through officials. 'Would Mr Allday like to name the date for the sale as well?' After that there was a lot less public talk about possible privatization, although the appointment of Christopher Harding as Con's successor in 1985 revived the speculation.

Christopher, a long-standing director of Hanson, had been

suggested to Peter Walker as a non-executive director and possible future Chairman of BNFL by Lord Hanson himself. Christopher made no secret of the fact that privatization was firmly on his agenda for BNFL – and that he would not have taken the Chairman's job if he had thought that the Government was not similarly inclined.

With the benefit of hindsight, it is now apparent that if any company had snapped up BNFL in the early days of the company's existence it would have been buying itself a can of worms. It had unresolved contractual problems from the day it started to trade in 1971. No decision had been taken about who was to pay for storing the long-lived wastes inherited from the twenty-year-old reprocessing programme associated with the separation of nuclear weapons materials at Sellafield, mainly because these costs were wrongly considered to be marginal.

Nor was there any formal contractual agreement in place between BNFL and the Ministry of Defence about who would pay for decommissioning the heavily contaminated buildings in which these weapons materials had been produced. At that time no agreement was considered necessary; it was assumed that costs would be small and that they could be left to be recovered as they were incurred.

The first public indication that there might be a problem came in the directors' report section of the 1976–7 annual report. The company stated that it had set aside a fund covering the estimated cost of vitrifying, as recommended by the Royal Commission on Environmental Pollution in the Flowers Report.

At 31 March 1977 BNFL tucked away £13 million as a deferred liability for this purpose, basing this figure on the latest technical assessment of the cost of vitrifying the highly radioactive waste products which had arisen since the formation of the company. The cost assessment exercise could not have been easy. The work was to be carried out in plants which had still to be designed and built, using technology which would take over a decade to develop.

But at least the new company was trying to cover its own future liabilities. No provision at all had been made for the potential cost of vitrifying the highly active waste products already on hand at the date of the company's formation. This figure was clearly going to be a great deal more significant than that acknowledged by BNFL itself. 'Whilst the amount on the same basis would be substantial, HM Government has informed the company that it will be prepared to discuss the question of how these latter costs should be met when they arise,' the annual report stated. This statement was drawn from what came to be known within BNFL as 'the letter of comfort' from the Government.

Great reliance was placed on this 'letter of comfort' by the company's directors and auditors over the years, although it contained no direct reference to how other potential costs, in addition to those associated with the vitrification of high-level waste, were to be met. Those costs included expenditure of many hundreds of millions of pounds on the packaging of intermediate- and low-level waste arising from the reprocessing carried out before 1971, of storing and eventually disposing of these wastes, and of decommissioning the old buildings in which military reprocessing had taken place.

BNFL's directors were becoming increasingly concerned about who was to meet these costs. In the 1977–8 report they made the point that a number of items arose under the heading of 'provisions and deferred liabilities' to which it was not possible to ascribe precise costs. Where possible, they explained, an assessment of liability had been made, based on the latest information available, but in other cases the existence of the potential liability could only be noted.

'These latter, very long-term costs arise either because development work has not yet reached the stage where firm assessments can be made or because the scope of the work required or the extent to which liability will fall on the company cannot at present be determined,' the report stated. 'However, the board is satisfied that any potential additional amounts which might be required can be met in future years without impairing the company's viability.' Given the considerable uncertainties surrounding so many aspects of the problem, the directors' confidence may be difficult to understand; they were clearly relying on the cost-plus trading arrangements in place for much of their business, together with discounting, to cover the position.

Three years further on and the directors were even more perturbed about the potential scale of the company's future liabilities. They realized that it was not only highly active wastes which would have to be packaged, by way of the vitrification process, but that the intermediate-level wastes (ILW), stored in water-filled silos such as the leaking B38, would also have to be encapsulated in cement and turned into solid packages, ready for disposal. Apart from the problem with B38 there had been a build-up of hydrogen in one of the other silos, threatening an explosion.

The directors also knew that disposal itself would cost more in real terms than had been anticipated in 1971 and they had begun to understand the extent of the decommissioning problem they had on their hands. In the 1981–2 annual report they pointed out that no provision had been made not only for vitrifying the highly active waste products on hand at the formation of the company eleven years earlier, but none had been made for the decommissioning of obsolete plants located on BNFL sites (not just Sellafield) when they were taken over in 1971 either. 'The amounts would be substantial. The question of how such costs should be met, when they arise, is under discussion with Government,' the report said.

Another two years passed by and the company felt able to say that the responsibility of the BNFL group for the long-term management of waste products and for the decommissioning of plants arising from programmes carried out prior to 1 April 1971 'has been clarified in discussion with the

Government'. An additional provision, which was not considered significant, had been made in accordance with the group's accounting policies. Although it had 'clarified' the position with the Government, BNFL did not settle the financial formula for recovering pre-1971 waste and decommissioning costs for the Ministry of Defence for another six years.

Neville Chamberlain, the Chief Executive, brought the matter to a head when he delayed publication of the 1987–8 accounts and threatened to publish them with a qualification which would show where the problem lay. A couple of days before Neville and the Chairman, Christopher Harding, were due to appear before the Public Accounts Committee of the House of Commons, the pre-1971 liability issue was finally settled – seventeen years after the formation of BNFL.

In the end the following words were agreed with the MoD and the Treasury: 'The company has embarked on construction of a series of waste treatment plants and a significant part of their throughput will relate to materials arising prior to the formation of the company for which HM Government has accepted liability in principle. Detailed negotiations on the basis for payment of their share of the relevant costs have yet to be completed, but it has been considered appropriate to include a sum of £25 million in the current year's operating profits to cover the cost of servicing the capital deployed on behalf of Government bodies in this and prior years.'

Apart from the pre-1971 wastes issue, another problem was stored up for the future when BNFL was formed. This concerned the mechanism which the Government agreed the new company should use to charge for its services. It was agreed that BNFL's trading profit from the supply of nuclear fuel services to the CEGB the SSEB should be established on the basis of a rate of return on the capital employed in the provision of those services. Any surplus or deficiency of actual profit earned over the rate of return basis would then be assessed at the end of each triennium and any necessary adjustments would be made at that time.

What that formula meant in practice was that all of BNFL's business with the CEGB and SSEB was to be on a cost-plus basis. Given this trading arrangement between monopolistic companies sharing public-sector status and the same shareholder it is not surprising that BNFL has made a profit in every year of its existence.

In the mid-1980s, with most of the uncertainties with regard to production programmes and capital and operating costs reduced to acceptable levels, BNFL took a new initiative to bring the cost-plus arrangement to an end. One of the first things Neville Chamberlain did when he was appointed Chief Executive in 1985 was to press the case for a move to fixed prices, despite opposition within his own company. He deserves considerable credit for it. Neville recognized that the terms of trading arrangements in force when he took over the company's reins could not possibly be in the longer-term interest of BNFL or its customers. They positively encouraged inefficiency within BNFL and made it extremely difficult to impose any sort of real cost discipline.

I have heard design engineers express amazement when the BNFL board complained that project costs had soared beyond the assessed final cost figure contained in their original capital expenditure proposals. Surely the board realized that the more projects cost, the greater the profit which would accrue to BNFL. It is not surprising in the circumstances that many of BNFL's plants at Sellafield are now considered to have been over-engineered. Similar arguments about costs being more than covered by customer payments came into play when there was any discussion of the need to reduce the company's wages bill and improve efficiency by reducing manning levels.

There was a monitoring arrangement in place which made it necessary for BNFL to justify expenditure on new plants in advance and to explain why cost overruns occurred. This led to heated arguments and ill-feeling, but there was a reasonable degree of confidence within BNFL that no matter how acrimonious these discussions became the CEGB and the SSEB would pick up their share of the tab in the end.

When Neville Chamberlain first raised the possibility of placing all of BNFL's business with them on a fixed price basis (but one which allowed for regular reviews covering the way the new system was working in practice) the CEGB and the SSEB were initially very suspicious. BNFL had only just signed contracts worth £1,600 million with the two generating boards covering 1,850 tonnes of oxide fuel reprocessing business in THORP – contracts which were then thought to be firm but which turned out not to be. This was eight years after the plant had been approved by the Government and well into THORP's construction programme and the signing of the contracts had come as a considerable relief to BNFL. The generators were therefore more than a little puzzled that BNFL should want to return to the commercial negotiating table.

Neville Chamberlain had recognized, however, that BNFL was not only unlikely to improve its efficiency while it could charge most of its costs out to customers at a guaranteed profit but that if the electricity supply industry was privatized the cost-plus arrangement would probably not survive. Investors pressing for commercial rates of return on capital would simply not find the practice acceptable.

The privatization of electricity supply was just being talked about when Neville raised the matter with the generating boards. The assumption then was that the CEGB and the SSEB would be privatized intact, including their nuclear power stations, and that after privatization they would remain BNFL's customers for the full range of nuclear fuel services.

The received wisdom from Whitehall was that the CEGB and SSEB were unlikely to be broken up – and certainly not into small pieces – because of the Government's conviction that the newly privatized companies had to be of a size which would enable them to maintain the costly development of nuclear power. This was regarded as essential for security of supply reasons, with the 1984 miners strike still fresh in Mrs Thatcher's memory, and because of nuclear power's environmental advantage over fossil fuels in respect of the greenhouse effect, which was also preoccupying the Prime Minister.

BNFL's negotiations with the CEGB and SSEB were overtaken by events when the nuclear power stations were pulled out of the Electricity Supply Industry (ESI) privatization at the last minute and Nuclear Electric and Scottish Nuclear were formed to take over the nuclear power stations, which remained in the public sector. I believe that it was a mistake to detach nuclear power from the ESI privatization and that the mistake was based largely on a false premise. This was that the cost of decommissioning nuclear power stations had been understated in the past. As a result, the Government, suddenly led to believe that decommissioning was much more expensive than it had been thought, did not dare to try to unload these costs on to the City. John Guinness, BNFL's current Chairman, was then Acting Permanent Secretary at the Department of Energy and was one of the people who advised Government to take nuclear power out of the ESI privatization exercise because of decommissioning costs.

The directors of BNFL were convinced that the CEGB, in particular, had overstated the problem in order to secure additional financial guarantees from the Government before the generating boards were privatized. I know that BNFL protested to the CEGB that this was giving a false impression of the cost of nuclear power, which the industry might come to regret.

Lord Marshall, the CEGB's Chairman, reminded BNFL that the CEGB was its biggest customer and that BNFL might be advised to stay out of the argument. Relationships between the CEGB and BNFL became increasingly strained during the build-up to the ESI privatization, with Walter Marshall complaining bitterly that BNFL's reprocessing costs were more likely to threaten the privatization of his nuclear power stations than the cost he had ascribed to decommissioning.

What was most worrying was that Lord Marshall was known to be personally enthusiastic about nuclear power, while some of his CEGB colleagues were beginning to say openly that nuclear power was more trouble than it was worth. They included John Baker, then the CEGB's Chief Executive and my Chairman at Nirex – now Chairman of National Power and still a critic of nuclear power costs and subsidies.

Neville Chamberlain had a very real concern that if the CEGB went into the private sector intact, with John Baker as its Chief Executive, there would never be another nuclear power station order in Britain. Neville persuaded the BNFL board that the company must start looking at the possibility of becoming a nuclear electricity generator in its own right, building on the somewhat limited experience of operating the small and old Calder Hall and Chapelcross Magnox reactors. In that way, Mr Chamberlain argued, BNFL would demonstrate its own continuing commitment to nuclear power and create a bigger market for the BNFL group's enrichment, fuel manufacturing and reprocessing services. It is called putting your money where your mouth is. Unfortunately, it also turned out to be an expensive diversion down a business cul-de-sac.

When BNFL began a feasibility study into the possibility of building PWR power stations in the Sellafield area and on the Chapelcross site I had my doubts about how far the company would be allowed to go by the Government. I could not believe that it would be allowed to compete with the newly-privatized CEGB without a fight and occasionally voiced my concern as the cost of pursuing Neville's dream mounted.

But the real opposition at the BNFL board, where the executive directors rarely argued among themselves, came from one of the non-executive directors, Jean Denton, who was later to become Baroness Denton and a Government minister. Jean pursued David Evans, the senior executive brought in from the UKAEA to run the reactor feasibility study, relentlessly about the market possibilities for the electricity from the new nuclear reactors – much to David's irritation. She was right to do so. We were virtually being asked to accept on trust that there would be a market well over a decade hence, when the station or stations might be completed. Several of us doubted that would be the case.

Nevertheless, some £30 million was ploughed into the feasibility study, which concluded in 1990 that a greenfield site at Starling Castle, near Sellafield, and BNFL's existing Chapelcross site over the Scottish border were suitable in principle for the construction of large PWRs of up to 1,500 megawatts' capacity.

The trouble was that the world had moved on by the time this conclusion was reached and Nuclear Electric and Scottish Nuclear had been formed out of the CEGB and SSEB to run Britain's nuclear power stations. And they were not at all keen on seeing BNFL enter the nuclear electricity generating market in competition with them. To make matters worse, as part of the electricity supply industry privatization the Government placed a four-year moratorium on new nuclear power station ordering.

BNFL was forced to back off and announced that it was talking to the two new nuclear generating companies about how the BNFL project could be integrated into the reactor building programme which they were trying to develop in advance of the Government's review of the nuclear industry, which would bring the moratorium to an end. BNFL even tried to get NE and SN to make a contribution towards the cost of its reactor feasibility study, without success.

It is unlikely that British Energy Limited, formed as a result of the Government's review, will ever be interested in building new stations at Sellafield and Chapelcross. Although they have the attraction of a measure of local goodwill, especially at Chapelcross, neither site is well placed in relation to the

National Grid even if the nuclear power construction programme is revived one day. The cost of its reactor feasibility study seems destined to become another expense which BNFL will have to write off to experience.

Ironically, the Government's decision to remove the nuclear power stations from the ESI privatization, taken because of what it was told by the CEGB about decommissioning costs, led to the resignation of Lord Marshall. Instead of becoming Chairman of National Power, as most of us expected, he joined the World Association of Nuclear Operators, formed after Chernobyl to help improve nuclear safety world-wide.

Walter Marshall's commanding presence and stimulating intellect has been sorely missed by the nuclear power industry. Unfortunately, he had to learn the lesson that in the final analysis public servants will lose any arguments they have with the politicians to whom they report, certainly if those arguments are conducted in public. Advised by Cecil Parkinson and later by John Wakeham that the City had no interest in the CEGB if it still owned nuclear power stations Mrs Thatcher backed her Cabinet colleagues. Nuclear power was side-lined.

Although BNFL kept quiet, as 'requested' by Lord Marshall, there is a hint of what BNFL really felt about the CEGB's claims about decommissioning costs in the run-up to the ESI privatization in the Chairman's statement in BNFL's 1988–9 annual report.

> The true cost of nuclear generated electricity, no matter how the bill is split between the electricity customer and the taxpayer, is never easy to determine. 'Long-term costs can only be estimated and the estimates are only as good as the assumptions on which they are based.
>
> 'The provisions needed now for the costs of decommissioning the existing stations will depend as much on timing as on the actual cost when the work is carried out. Sensible deferment to allow radioactive decay to simplify

the technical challenge, and reduce radiation doses to the workers involved, will lower both the real cost then and the cost now of making appropriate financial provision for it.'

It came as no great surprise to me that in its 1995 White Paper the Government was able to say that experience with the early stages of decommissioning at three Magnox power stations had demonstrated that the cost estimates made for decommissioning by the CEGB and the SSEB in 1989 (not NE and SN as the White Paper says) were extremely pessimistic, as BNFL always suspected.

Actual costs for the first stage of decommissioning at Berkeley, where dismantling is most advanced, have been about one-third lower than originally estimated by the CEGB and this experience is mirrored at the other two stations, Hunterston A and Trawsfynydd.

It is no surprise, of course, that this time round the Government and the nuclear generating companies are both desperately keen to show that decommissioning costs are not an insurmountable obstacle to the privatization of the AGRs and the PWRs. It should also be borne in mind that these are still early days as far as decommissioning cost estimates are concerned.

When the nuclear power stations were taken out of the ESI privatization there was some suggestion that BNFL should drop the idea of moving to fixed price contracts for the supply of its nuclear fuel services. There were those in all of the companies involved who argued that there was no immediate need for change, as Nuclear Electric, Scottish Nuclear and BNFL were all to remain in the public sector for at least four years and probably longer. Neville Chamberlain persisted, however, and not only because of the earlier reasons he had identified to the BNFL board about the need to improve efficiency. By now he had become convinced that BNFL could only prosper as an international nuclear fuels business if it had the internal discipline of fixed price contracts.

On the formation of NE and SN, BNFL had no firm fuel cycle contracts with either of the new companies. All it had was the set of fixed price offers for its fuel services which it had made to the CEGB and SSEB when it was still thought that those two companies would be privatized intact. For the next six years the three companies traded on the basis of these offers rather than any firm agreements, preparing their accounts accordingly and making it clear in successive annual reports that whatever was finally agreed would apply retrospectively from 1 April 1989.

By February 1992 it looked as though a deal was imminent. Principles of Agreement had been signed between BNFL and NE and between BNFL and SN, based on the Government underwriting the risks implicit in the long periods which the contracts were intended to last. Government underwriting would have had an added advantage for the three companies. A Government providing financial guarantees against the risk of regulatory changes in the health, safety and environmental protection areas affecting the cost of BNFL's services could be expected to think twice before imposing new and expensive restrictions unnecessarily, for example as a knee-jerk political reaction after some incident at Sellafield.

So sure were the three companies that they would get this underwriting, which the Government had been aware the companies wanted for over three years, that Neville Chamberlain felt able to announce publicly that he had concluded a series of deals with Nuclear Electric and Scottish Nuclear covering nearly two-thirds of BNFL's business. Henceforth, BNFL's nuclear fuel cycle services – the provision of new fuel and the reprocessing of spent fuel from the NE and SN Magnox and AGR power stations, including spent fuel for THORP – would be provided under tightly negotiated fixed-price contracts relating to business worth some £17,000 million.

These contracts would cover BNFL's business with NE and SN for the next fifteen years and Neville Chamberlain could say with some confidence: 'Our future income is largely secured; whether we prosper or not now depends on how well we control our costs.' Unfortunately, whatever documentary evidence there was to support this statement was as worthless as the scrap of paper Mr Chamberlain's namesake brought back from Munich before the Second World War.

Two months after contractual peace had broken out between BNFL, NE and SN the Government pulled the rug from under the three companies. It decided that as they were all owned by the Government this was guarantee enough. As their sole shareholder, the Government could decide to bail out one or more of the three companies if they got into financial difficulties, or it could let them go to the wall.

The decision was a bombshell to all three companies and I began to wonder what plans the Government really had for nuclear power, particularly as the announcement that there would be no Government underwriting coincided with the appointment of John Guinness, a civil servant, as BNFL's Chairman in succession to Sir Christopher Harding. That was seen by some of us as a signal that while the Government might privatize the nuclear power generating companies on a reasonably short time-scale it had no such plans for BNFL.

On his arrival at BNFL Mr Guinness protested that this was not the case. I was not convinced. My suspicions were reinforced at the end of 1994, shortly after I had finally detached myself from BNFL, when the Government announced that the company was to become subject to the Public Sector Borrowing Requirement (PSBR) regime. The reason given for this, that it was no more than a matter of statistical convenience, simply did not hold water. The BNFL board had always been aware that there were those in the Treasury who wanted BNFL inside the PSBR, where detailed control could be exercised over investment policy. John Guinness's predecessors had all fought the Treasury off.

In retirement, and therefore free to argue in public, Con Allday continued to insist that placing BNFL outside the PSBR on the company's formation had worked to the Government's as well as the company's advantage. Outside the PSBR it had been possible for the company to raise funds for its massive capital expenditure programme, including THORP, through loans from the European Investment Bank and the City, customer prepayments and internal self-financing. Even though the company's bank loans were underwritten by the Government no liability had ever materialized in this respect. BNFL had also managed to pay the Government a total of £400 million in dividends over the twenty-three years it existed outside the PSBR and had increased the value of the Government's original equity investment of £33 million to £700 million during the same period.

My original theory when I heard of the Government's decision to put BNFL inside the PSBR was that it was doing so because the company was about to generate considerable funds and become cash-rich with the operation of THORP. Later, I became more and more convinced that the real message to be drawn from the PSBR announcement was that BNFL was destined to remain in the public sector for all time.

The idea that it might also assume responsibility for the Magnox stations owned by Nuclear Electric and Scottish Nuclear had not occurred to me in December 1993 when BNFL bounced back with a new formula for fixed-price contracts with NE and SN. These were based on BNFL bearing the risks on Magnox and AGR fuel supply and reprocessing services, but with the Government still underwriting the risks on historic wastes and the decommissioning of old plants. Even this was too much for the Government to swallow, however.

By July 1994 BNFL was forced to accept that the Government was not prepared to provide any form of underwriting and began to talk to Nuclear Electric again. In November negotiations also resumed between BNFL and Scottish

Nuclear, and the scope of the intended deal was extended to cover the reprocessing or storage by BNFL of spent AGR fuel which SN had previously intended to dry-store itself.

At long last, there appeared to be a deal which was for real. On 30 March 1995 BNFL and Scottish Nuclear signed fixed-price contracts worth some £4,000 million. A day later BNFL and Nuclear Electric signed contracts worth £14,000 million. BNFL, it seemed, had finally sewn up £18,000 million worth of UK business. Unfortunately, these contracts were rendered partially useless, perhaps even totally worthless, within a bare six weeks of them being signed when the Government announced its privatization proposals for NE and SN, leaving BNFL in the public sector. I have confirmed that the three companies had no idea what lay ahead for them during their negotiations, although it seems incredible that they should be kept completely in the dark.

It is probable that those sections of the contracts relating to the long-term supply by BNFL of new fuel for the AGR and PWR power stations which are to be owned by British Energy Limited will survive the unscrambling process which is now having to be undertaken.

It may even be that the fixed-price contracts signed by NE and SN for some of their spent AGR fuel to be reprocessed in THORP will be honoured by BEL as well, although the time-scales are so long that it would not surprise me if the new company tried to obtain further price concessions. Some renegotiation would be necessary, of course, if BEL decided to commit all of its AGR and PWR spent fuel to THORP, as I have advocated.

But six years of painstaking negotiations between BNFL, Nuclear Electric and Scottish Nuclear over Magnox fuel supply and reprocessing charges were rendered a total waste of time and money when it was announced that BNFL was to be given responsibility for the operation and decommissioning of all the Magnox stations.

That piece of nonsense had all the ingredients of a Whitehall farce. It is to be hoped that the reorganization of the nuclear industry which is now taking place will not develop into another.

Epilogue

I thought long and hard before deciding to go ahead with this book. Most of my friends urged me not to do so. They felt that the book's publication would lead to further public interest in how my career in nuclear power was brought to an end and to little else. Their concern was based on a misconception, however. Because I have not described the events leading up to my resignation previously they assumed that the issue would come to dominate my book. I was determined that should not happen.

There are aspects of the affair which will always disturb me and I feel very strongly that I was let down badly by some of my colleagues. But sufficient time has elapsed for me to feel able to push the matter to one side and treat the far more important subject of nuclear power with the objectivity it deserves. That has certainly been my intention. However, I felt that if I ducked the issue entirely my silence might be used to discredit my views on what went wrong with the troubled industry which the Government is now desperately trying to privatize.

I resigned from BNFL in March 1993 after it had been put to me by my employers that the cost of decorating and minor repair work carried out for me by contractors, who also worked for BNFL, had been charged to the company. I accepted that statement in good faith, while making it clear that if this had happened it was done without my knowledge. That remains my position.

There was nothing unusual about contractors working for BNFL employees. Several of the directors and other members of staff had work done for them by contractors during the eighteen years I worked for the company. The issue was solely one of whether BNFL had been charged for services I had received and whether I was aware this had happened. An internal investigation into the administration of the relevant contract lasted for several months and involved dozens of people. During it a contract administrator employed by BNFL committed suicide.

At the time I was not only doing my normal job but also leading the THORP campaign and preparing to move to London to take on the task of coordinating the nuclear industry's attempt to get a favourable result from the Government's review of nuclear power. The further pressure of finding myself involved in an internal investigation became too much for me. I came to the conclusion that my position had been made untenable by the rumours surrounding the affair and I resigned. And there the matter would have rested if my resignation had been accepted immediately by the company. But instead of providing me with the resignation terms we had agreed, the company – prompted by the Department of Trade and Industry – called in the Cheshire police to investigate the matter. Meanwhile I was effectively suspended and continued to receive my salary.

In March 1994 I was cleared. In fact, no charges were brought against anyone. My resignation terms were finally implemented and my pension was actually uprated to reflect the extra year I had 'worked' for BNFL while sitting at home.

Those are the bare bones of the story and I am sure that BNFL felt – and continues to feel – that I was treated fairly in the circumstances. I cannot accept that. I asked BNFL to show me its evidence that some of my costs had gone to the company several times before and after I resigned. It took BNFL five months to provide me with the information I sought. I have never been given an explanation for the delay.

When I eventually received BNFL's 'evidence' it consisted solely of time-sheets put in to BNFL by contractors' workers. Those time-sheets were flawed, if not downright fraudulent. The sheets were said to cover the labour costs associated with the most recent work done for me, when I had used one of the contractors to prepare my new house for occupation.

Although the work had not been finished, I had given the contractor a cheque for £2,500 for the work carried out up to the time I heard about the BNFL internal audit and had been told that my final bill might be as high as £3,000. I thought that was more than enough to cover the labour costs involved. But BNFL told me that the company had been charged £7,720 by the contractor for this work and invoiced me for that amount. I thought the bill was outrageous and challenged it, but was persuaded by Neville Chamberlain to pay up in order to clear the matter.

It was the size of that bill which led me to accept the later assertion by BNFL that bills associated with previous work carried out for me by contractors over the years were too low and that other costs had found their way to the company.

I do not know when the time-sheets sent to me were filled in or under what conditions, but as soon as I went through them I knew they were false. They purported to show that a total of 631 working hours were spent by workmen on fitting out and decorating a conventional four-bedroom house, using materials which I had paid for separately.

I can show through delivery notes and invoices for these

materials that much of this work could not have been done on the dates specified. I can also prove that work was not done by the number of workmen said to have been involved and that the hours they supposedly worked were greatly exaggerated. As an example of the sort of nonsense contained in those time-sheets, they indicated that floor tiles and light fittings which had not been bought were installed in a conservatory which had not been built.

I also tested the £7,270 invoice passed on to me by BNFL by obtaining two alternative quotations for the work involved from other contractors in the Warrington area, chosen at random from *Yellow Pages*. If I had accepted the lower of the two estimates I could have had the work done for less than £2,000 – and that is without haggling – and the higher estimate was still well below the £2,500 I had originally paid the BNFL contractor.

Because of what I have discovered since I left BNFL I am no longer convinced that any of my costs were passed on to the company. I have certainly never been shown any evidence to support that contention. As a result I will always feel that I was misled into resigning. Despite everything that had happened, at the end of 1995 Neville Chamberlain invited me to join past and present directors of BNFL for a Christmas lunch at Risley. I am sure the gesture was a well intentioned attempt to rebuild bridges, but I declined the invitation.

I do not know how '*Inside Sellafield*' will be received within BNFL. But I do know what my approach to the nuclear power issues I have discussed within it is totally in line with the policy of openness and honesty which I introduced into BNFL.

My former colleagues can hardly complain about that.